Famous South African
Folk Tales

Famous South African
Folk Tales

Selected and retold by
Pieter W. Grobbelaar
Illustrations by Séan Verster

Human & Rousseau
Cape Town   Pretoria   Johannesburg

First revised edition 2003
Third edition 1993
Second edition 1984
First edition 1968

Copyright © 1968 in text by Pieter W Grobbelaar
Copyright © 2002 in illustrations by Séan Verster
Published by Human & Rousseau, 28 Wale Street,
Cape Town
Designed and set in 11 on 15 pt Bookman
by ALINEA STUDIO, Cape Town
Printed and bound by Colorcraft, Hong Kong
ISBN 07981 4265 0

Contents

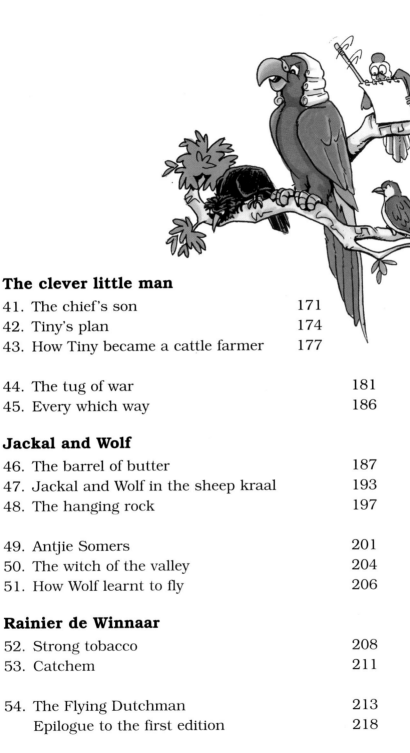

The ungrateful snake

The pine forest was on fire. The flames licked greedily through the dry pine needles on the ground and danced in the treetops. When Puffadder opened his lazy eyes, it was too late. Already the flames were all around him. He tried this side, he tried that side, but every way was closed.

Just then a farmer dived through the smoke. He was busy beating out the flames with a wet sack.

"Farmer, Farmer!" called Puffadder. "Help me! I'm burning to death."

"Burn away," said Farmer. "If I help you out, you'll only bite me."

"That I would never do!" promised Puffadder. "Just help me. Help me!"

The farmer felt sorry for Puffadder. He held the mouth of the sack open so that the snake could slip in, and carried him out of danger.

But when Puffadder lay safely on the cool ground, he reared up and said, "Aha, now I've got you. I have wanted your blood for a long time." And he drew his head back for the deathblow.

"No, you can't do that!" shouted Farmer. "You promised."

"I can't help

it if you're a fool," said Puffadder, and he hissed venomously.

"Let's first hear what others think about it," asked Farmer.

"All right," said Puffadder, because he would enjoy terrorising Farmer a little while longer.

So they came to Cow where she was grazing in the field.

"Cow, Cow, I saved this snake from the fire, and now he wants to bite me," complained Farmer.

Cow looked up. "A cow must eat and give milk," said she. "And a snake must bite and kill. No, what Puffadder says is right."

"There, you see!" said Puffadder, and he raised his head again.

"Let's ask Horse too," said Farmer.

Horse neighed with pleasure when he heard the story. "Farmer's spurs are always biting into me if I don't gallop fast enough," he said. "No, I think it will be a good thing if you get that blow in, Puffadder."

"Do you hear that?" hissed Puffadder.

"Seems to me Cow and Horse don't like me," said Farmer sorrowfully. "And it is I who always see to it that they have enough food and sleep warmly at night. You animals are all ungrateful. Strike then, if you must."

But just then Jackal came trotting by. "What's going on here?" he demanded.

Farmer told his story.

Jackal scratched his head. "Farmer was in the sack and Puffadder carried him out," he repeated.

"No, no," said Farmer. "Puffadder was in the sack."

Now Jackal was completely bewildered. "But how could Puffadder be in the sack? It was on fire, wasn't it?"

"You're being silly, Jackal!" called Puffadder. "The forest was on fire, and Farmer let me slip into the sack!"

"Oh, Farmer was on fire, and the forest slipped into the sack," Jackal began again. "No, the forest was in the sack, and Puffadder . . ." Jackal shook his head. "I'm sorry, but you'll have to show me what happened, Puffadder. All this talk makes my head spin."

"Then look carefully," said Puffadder furiously. "You're wasting my time, and I want to kill." His thick body slipped into the sack until only his thin tail stuck out. "Do you see now?" he called from inside, but Jackal sprang forward, grabbed the sack and said, "There now, everything is as it was. Take the sack, Farmer, and be careful that Puffadder doesn't talk you round again."

"You can be sure he won't!" said Farmer. "Thank you very much. And tonight you're welcome to a fat hen – I'll tie up the dogs."

"Thank you," said Jackal, and he trotted off.

"Let me out! Let me out!" shouted Puffadder from the sack. "Jackal tricked me!"

"You tricked your- self," said Farmer. He found a good, thick stick and beat Puffadder to death.

The seal maiden

Very late one evening a fisherman, tired after the day's catch, was walking along the shore. The full moon had just climbed over the mountain, and suddenly he saw something moving in the water. Seven seals dived out of the waves and wriggled up onto the sand. They threw their skins aside, and now they were seven young maidens, their bodies shining in the moonlight as they danced. The fisherman stood bewitched, and he forgot all else. But when the church clock in the village struck twelve, the seal maidens picked up their skins and disappeared into the waves, laughing.

Now the fisherman watched every evening for the maidens. He had seen them once, and he could not forget them. But, watch as he would, it was full moon again before they appeared. This time he crept a little closer. He saw their long, wet hair like seaweed in the wind, and he heard their song, wild and deep like a storm at sea, then light and clear like a ripple in rock pools – but he understood not a word they sang.

With the third full moon he dared to go so close that he could look into their eyes, shining clear as water. He desper-

ately longed to be one of them, but he knew that if they ever saw him, they would never come back. So he waited his chance, crept up to the heap of skins, stole one and buried it in the sand.

At twelve o'clock the dance ended. Six sisters snatched their skins and ran across the sand, but the seventh sought in vain.

"Sisters! Sisters!" she called. "My skin has gone!"

"Sister, sister!" they answered. "Make haste, we cannot stay longer!"

The seal maiden stumbled among the sand dunes. "Sisters, sisters!" she pleaded.

"Sister, sister!" they called from the waves.

The seal maiden fell down, sobbing. "Sisters, sisters!" she wept.

"Sister, sister . . ." came the faraway reply.

Up came the fisherman. "Can I help?" he asked.

"My skin, my sealskin. Have you seen it?" she begged.

"No," he answered, "but come with me. I have a house and all you need. I'll care for you and make you happy."

"I shall never be happy again," answered the seal maiden, but she followed him.

So the fisherman and the seal maiden were married. In time they had two children, two little girls, with their mother's sea-green eyes and the same golden hair. The fisherman was very careful. He dug up the skin he had stolen, took it and locked it in the cellar, and he kept the key with him always.

The seal maiden was a good mother. No one would have said she was not human. Only in the evening, when she put her children to bed and sang them a lullaby, did the fisherman become uneasy. For then again he heard the sound of the waves in her voice – the same sound he had heard when she had danced with her sisters on the sands. She sang:

Far is the land where the sisters dwell,
Where they turn and twist in the waters' swell,
Where the coils of weed twine legs and hands,
While they linger all day on golden sands.

16

Oh, far is the land for which I long,
Where to the wind and the waters' song,
They nightly dance on the silver strand.
Oh, far, so far is the Faraway Land.

The years passed, the children grew up, and their mother sang no more. Her golden hair was touched with grey, and her eyes were dimmed. The fisherman thought: now, now she has surely forgotten. But still he carried the key with him always, though he was not quite so careful with it. And so it came about that one day he left the house in a hurry because the wind was blowing hard, and he feared that it might damage his boat. This time he left the key at home.

The seal maiden had never again spoken of her lost skin, but that day, when she held the unknown key in her hand, it was as if something was drawing her. Quickly, without even having to search, she went straight to the cellar. She opened the door. There lay the skin. She caught it up in her arms. Suddenly the wind blew gold in her hair, and the light of the moon shone deep in her eyes. Her children, who had missed her and came looking for her, drew back in fear of what they saw.

"Mother, Mother!" they called.

"Farewell, my children," said the seal maiden, and she moved quickly towards the sea.

"Do not leave us, Mother!" begged the girls.

"I cannot stay," answered the seal maiden, and she moved even faster.

"Mother, Mother!" sobbed the girls.

But the last that they saw of her was a gleam of white on the sand when she threw off her clothes and put on the sealskin. And the last that they heard of her was the echo of her song out of the waves:

Far is my Land of Faraway,
Where on the silvery sand they play
To the sound of the wind and the waters' song.
I come, oh land for which I long.

When the fisherman returned, he saw that his wife had gone. His children then told him what had happened and he knew that to seek her would be useless. Only when the full moon shone at night, his heart wanted to break, and he would go down to the beach to see if the seal maidens had not come again. But they had found other shores on which to spend the silvery hours in dancing – far from the prying eyes of humans and the grasping hands of fishermen, there in the Land of Faraway.

19

Pinkie

Long, long ago, on a farm far from here, lived a young man who was very small. He was no bigger than the farmer's little finger, so everyone called him Pinkie.

Pinkie was the shepherd. By day he sat on an ant heap, sunning himself. So small was he that no one would know he was there. But if a thief came along, Pinkie called out in a big voice, "Don't steal my sheep!" The thief looked round, but saw nothing. But let him try again. Then Pinkie shouted in his deep voice, "If I catch you, I'll skin you alive!" The thief was so frightened that he made off. "Ho, ho, ho," laughed Pinkie, and he turned a somersault with joy.

But Pinkie also got up to all sorts of tricks. When the farmer called his workers to him, Pinkie crept up their trouser legs and tickled them until they laughed. Then the farmer got very cross, because he thought they were laughing at him; he did not know that they were laughing because of Pinkie.

At night Pinkie slept just wherever he happened to be. If the farmer's jacket was left hanging over a chair, Pinkie made a bed of the pocket. When the nights got colder, he sheltered deep in a shoe. Sometimes he went to visit Piebald, the milk cow. He had a drink straight from her teat, then crept deep into a bundle of straw in the loft.

Now it happened that one night Pinkie lay so comfortably in the straw that he completely overslept. While he was still rubbing his eyes, the milkman threw Piebald her fodder. Before he could jump out of the way, the cow had gulped him down. The path was dark and smooth, and Pinkie slipped head over heels down Piebald's throat.

"Heigh-ho!" he sighed, just as the milkman came up with his bucket.

"I say!" said the milkman. "That's strange; it sounds to me as if this cow can talk today." He was not absolutely sure, though. "Move, Piebald!" he said, pushing her hind leg so she would step back and he could get the bucket under her udder.

"Move yourself!" called Pinkie from inside.

"There's big trouble today!" said the milkman, and he went to call the farmer.

The farmer came to look. "What's the matter with you, Piebald?" he asked.

"I want a better cowshed, for mine is too cold. I want a bet-ter milkman, for this fellow is scared too easily. And I want a better master, for mine is too silly to see what's wrong," answered Pinkie on the cow's behalf.

"No, a talking cow is not for me," said the farmer. "We'll slaughter her immediately."

All went well until a man cut the belly open. "Look out, blockhead!" shouted Pinkie. "If you touch me with that knife, you'll lose your own skin today." The man dropped everything and ran for help.

"I've never heard of a cow belly that can talk," said the farmer, and he started cutting it open himself. But Pinkie had, in the meanwhile, fled to the big intestine, and the farmer found nothing wrong. While the intestines were scraped and stuffed with sausage meat, Pinkie made sure that he came to no harm. Then he had nothing to complain about. The sausage meat, seasoned in farm style, tasted very good as it dried in the wind.

Every morning the farmer's wife fried some of the sausage for breakfast. One day it was the turn of Pinkie's piece. When it got hot in the pan, he called out, "Hey, you, turn the sausage!"

"Yes, husband," said the farmer's wife. She thought that it was the farmer who had spoken.

Then Pinkie's other side got hot. "Turn the sausage!" he screeched.

"I am turning it," said the woman, and she went up to the pan.

But Pinkie had been burnt enough. "Dish up! The sausage is ready!" he roared.

"My goodness, you're fussy today," said the woman, and she dished up. Pinkie landed on the farmer's plate.

The farmer's knife just missed Pinkie's nose.

"Whew, that was close," said Pinkie and heaved a sigh of relief.

The farmer cut again, and this time his knife went down just behind Pinkie's back.

"Now this is too much!" Pinkie complained.

"No, woman," said the farmer. "I'm not eating a talking sausage." And he threw the whole piece out of the window. Old Shepherd, the dog, would have snapped it up immediately, but Pinkie shouted just in time, "Be off!" – and Shepherd thought better of eating it. Pinkie crept out quickly and ran to the kitchen, where the farmer found him sitting on the hearth.

"Now then, Pinkie!" said the farmer, delighted. "Where've you been all the time?"

"First I got lost in a dark cave," Pinkie told him. "Then a giant came and cut the cave's roof open. I fled into a side passage, and there I was safe for a while. But the giant was a cannibal, and I've only just slipped out from between his teeth, otherwise I would've been dead."

"Whatever are you talking about?" laughed the farmer. "There are no giants or cannibals here. But I'm glad you're back. I need a man for the sheep."

And from that day on Pinkie was a shepherd again.

Bluebottle and Bee

Bluebottle and Bee were once brothers. Together they flew out every morning; together they sucked nectar from the flowers; together they brought it back to the hive.

Bee was as hard-working as they come. But Bluebottle was a shirker, always flying a few paces behind Bee, always sitting longer on a flower, and always bringing back less nectar.

One autumn morning out they flew again. The world was brown and bare. No trace of colour from a flower was to be seen anywhere.

"Bee," said Bluebottle after a while, pretending to be out of breath, "I can't go any further."

"Let's rest a bit then," said Bee, and he settled on a branch. "But we must not waste time. The days are getting short, and we have far to go."

"Yes," sighed Bluebottle, "we have a hard life, forever having to find food to take back to the hive for the little ones. Just look at Fly. He sits sunning himself all day. When he gets hungry, he quickly slips into Man's house and stuffs himself. Fly is clever. He knows how to get Man to do his work for him. We're the stupid ones. We work for ourselves, and for Man as well! Our pantry's scarcely full before he empties it again."

"What nonsense you talk," said Bee angrily. "We aren't flies that live on others' leftovers. We make our own food – and so well that even Man's kings are happy to have it on their tables. You should be proud of it."

"What use is pride to me?" asked Bluebottle. "I can't eat it."

"Come on, let's go!" said Bee.

"You go," said Bluebottle. "I'm still too tired."

Scarcely had Bee gone, when Bluebottle flew off too. He went straight to a rich man's house that Fly had told him about.

He flew around the house a few times, because he was still scared. Then he smelt food and dived in through the open window. He was in the kitchen. A big bowl of pudding stood on the table. Greedily he started eating.

But he forgot that he could not glide through the air as quietly as Fly. He buzzed just like his brother Bee.

The cook heard him and looked up. "I've just killed all the flies," he said, "and here's another one." Then his eyes widened. "It's Bee's brother," he said, surprised. "Are you also too lazy to find your own food now?" With one blow he swept Bluebottle out of the window.

Bluebottle was sorry that he could not eat more, but he was also very pleased with himself. He had never had such an easy meal before.

From then on he got even lazier. When he and Bee flew out to the rich man's house, his wing suddenly became lame or he had a cramp in his foot. Then, when Bee had gone, he flew into the kitchen as quickly as he could. Of course, there was not always pudding. Sometimes there were only a few dirty plates with leftovers.

Bluebottle's new life changed him completely. His body was no longer the golden brown of sun and earth like Bee's. It became bluish green like the mould on old bread. His voice was no longer the clear buzz of a hard worker. It became the grumble of a lazy glutton who asked continually, "Food, food, give me food." He was no longer a fighter like Bee who bravely defended himself against attackers. He became a coward who fled when he heard anyone approach. In a dark corner he crouched, lurking there and peering out until the danger had passed. His sting shrank and soon fell off completely.

"Bluebottle, this can't go on," said Bee one day when he arrived at the hive. "You'll have to find another home. We have nothing in common any more."

"That's fine," groaned Bluebottle who had just eaten much too much of the rich man's leftovers. "For a long time now I've wanted to move closer to my food."

Grumbling, he flew back to the rich man's kitchen and slipped in through the window. He crept in high against the cornice under the ceiling and settled himself for the night. He was half asleep when something moved next to him. It was Fly. "Welcome, Bluebottle," he said. But Bluebottle only groaned. He was too tired to answer.

And so it came about that bees today still make food fit for kings, while blowflies must be satisfied to lick the poorest man's plate.

The woman who could not hold her peace

In a wattle-and-daub hut near the beach lived a man and his wife. The house was small with a thatched roof, and the walls were of clay and sticks, for the two of them were poor. Every evening the man set his trap for hares and threw out his fishing line, and they lived on what he caught.

Early one morning, after he had taken a hare out and pulled a fish in, the man saw something in the sand. He began to dig, and what did he find but an iron trunk. He opened it and it was filled with money. He knew it must have come from a ship that had been wrecked on the rocks. And he knew that he must hand it in, because that was what the law said. But he was so poor and the gold shone so brightly that he could not bring himself to do that. He decided to keep it for himself.

There was just one problem. His wife talked too much. She would never be able to keep the secret. Many a time he had told her, "Go slow, woman. One day you'll land us in trouble with your foolish tongue." So quickly he made a plan. He hooked the dead hare on the fishhook and threw it into the sea, and he put the fish into the trap. Then he went to call his wife.

His wife was overjoyed when she saw all the money. She wanted to stuff it into her pockets then and there, but the man stopped her. "Just go and see if there's anything in the trap while I dig the trunk loose," he said.

In a little while his wife came back with the fish. "Husband," she said, "here's a queer thing. Look, I found a fish in the trap."

"That's queer indeed," said her husband. "Quick, go and look what's on the fishing line while I lift out the trunk."

In two twos the woman came running back, holding the hare in her hands. "Husband, this is really strange. I pulled out a hare on the hook."

"Yes, that is very strange," said her husband. "It must be because we've got money that such strange things are happening to us."

"That must be it," said the woman, and she helped to load the trunk onto the man's back.

Just then a man who had been swimming came out of the water. The breeze was cold, and he jumped up and down while drying himself.

"Who's that?" asked the woman inquisitively.

"Can't you see?" answered her husband. "That's the magistrate dancing the foxtrot."

"Oh!" said the woman, and off they went.

From then on the two of them lived well. There was money for everything: enough food, clothes and beautiful, new furniture. The man even had the house whitewashed. He did not want to leave it, because he loved the little place. His wife was not happy at all. She was bursting to tell someone the story, but her husband forbade her to talk and kept his eye on her night and day.

But in the evening as they sat before the fire, and the owl on the roof asked, "Hoo, hoo, hoo?" she could hold it in no longer.

"The little trunk that was washed off the ship. The trunk of money that we picked up. The trunk of money made us rich. That's who did it."

And her husband let her talk her fill. She got it off her chest and did no harm.

Then one day her neighbour came to visit again, and secretly she asked who gave them the money. This time the woman whispered, "Come this evening when the moon has set. Hoot at the window like an owl. Then I'll tell you."

That evening the neighbour brought her husband with her. "Hoo, hoo?" she hooted at the window. "Hoo, hoo, hoo?" hooted her husband.

Quickly the woman answered. "It was the iron trunk from the ship. It was the money that was washed ashore. It was the gold we found. That's who made us rich." Then she felt much better. But her neighbours were very envious. Early the next morning they went to town to tell the magistrate, and he sent the police to fetch the man and his wife.

"And what is this I hear of a little trunk full of money?" asked the magistrate as they stood before him.

"Let my wife tell the story, you Honour," said the man. "She's more than willing to talk."

"Where did you get the trunk?" asked the magistrate.

"On the beach, your Honour," answered the wife.

"When?" asked the magistrate.

"The morning when the fish was in the trap," said the woman.

"That's impossible," said the magistrate.

"And the hare was on the fish-hook," said the woman.

"Now, that's absurd," said the magistrate.

"It was the morning that your Honour danced the foxtrot on the beach," said the woman.

"You talk nonsense, woman!" said the magistrate, furious. "Take yourselves off, and don't let me see you again!"

"Thank you, your Honour," said the man, and they went home.

From then on the woman told her story to everyone who came, even though no one believed her. Her husband just laughed, for he knew the truth. And they were both very happy.

Captain Van Hunks and the Devil

A sailing ship docked in Table Bay, and a very big man came ashore. He was six feet two inches tall, with broad shoulders and the neck of a bull. And he looked such an important gentleman too. He had on a doublet of the finest silk, the buttons real rubies. The silver buckles on his shoes flashed in the sun. A long peacock's feather was stuck in his hatband.

People crowded around, curious.

"Is not that old Van Hunks?" called someone who had had a good look.

"Where did he get all that stuff?" asked another.

Old Van Hunks did not say a word. But his face got redder and redder, and the veins on his neck swelled purple. Then the sailors started to unload. Trunks and chests, and more chests and trunks. Perhaps they contained treasures, perhaps rubbish. But he was certainly very concerned about them.

The people of Cape Town remembered all about him. In the olden days he had been the Governor's huntsman. Then suddenly he had vanished without a trace. In those times he had been as poor as a pauper. And look at him now! How could it have happened?

People began to ask around, quietly in corners, and secretly in one of the taverns where the sailors drank. How had he done it? Such a scoundrel! Heads were shaken, fists were clenched, teeth were gnashed.

"Sailing under the skull and crossbones," said one.

"A real pirate!" said another.

"Certainly no captain of an ordinary ship," said a third.

"A child of the Devil!" they all agreed. "May the Devil take him!"

But Captain Van Hunks did not take any notice of all this talk. He went off to the Windberg, to the little house that had waited for him all the years. In those days the Cape was still young, but the captain had grown old. He had come to spend his last days there.

So he lived alone in his house, with one or two slaves to look after his cattle, and one for his garden. When the weather was bad, he sat on the stoep with his calabash pipe in his mouth, and a little barrel of arrack beside him. But on fine days he climbed up the Windberg, and there he sat smoking, drinking and looking far across the bay. He loved to watch the white sails of the ships filling in the wind as they came in to dock. But he dared not go near the harbour. There were too many sailors who might know him and who could prove dangerous.

Late one afternoon the old captain sat there as usual, when

suddenly he became aware of a stranger beside him. He had not seen him come, nor did he know who he was. But the man clearly knew him, because he greeted him as a friend, "Good afternoon, Captain Van Hunks."

"Good day," said Van Hunks curtly, and he pulled on his pipe, but the stranger was not put off by his bad manners.

"A pleasant place to sit," said the stranger, and he sat down himself.

"Yes," said the captain.

"A pleasant place to smoke," the stranger went on, and he took out his own pipe.

"Yes, yes!" said Captain Van Hunks.

A queer figure this stranger was. Long and thin and he was wearing a very tall top hat. There was not a trace of colour in his hollow cheeks, and black shadows lurked in his dark eyes.

He lit up. With the smoking, they came to talking, and from talking they went to boasting.

"I'm the heaviest smoker!"

"No, I am!"

"I am!"

"Well then, let's see who is," said the stranger, and he emptied his tobacco pouch onto a flat stone.

"Yes, let's," said the captain and turned his pouch out too.

"We must smoke for a prize," the stranger went on. "For your eternal soul, if I win. And I'll give you all the kingdoms of the earth if I lose."

"I lost my soul a long time ago already," growled the old sea captain. "And I've seen enough of earthly kingdoms. They're just trouble the livelong day. No, we'll smoke for the joy of it – to see who's the greatest smoker."

The tobacco was divided equally. Each had a small mountain in front of him, for they both had capacious pouches.

They knocked their pipes out. The tinderboxes lay ready.

Go!

Ram it down. Light up. Take a good pull. The old captain smoked with great enjoyment. So did the stranger.

They smoked till the sun had set and darkness came. They smoked till the cocks crowed. In-between the old captain told stories of pirates. The stranger listened, but did not speak.

Later on the smoke hung in a thick cloud over the slopes of the Windberg. Driven by the wind, it spread over the flat top of Table Mountain next to them.

"Look at that!" a French ship's captain, who had just arrived in the bay, called out. "The mountain's wearing a powdered wig."

"No," said the people of Cape Town, "it's a tablecloth for the Table Mountain."

They smoked the whole day. They smoked the following night. The cloud cloth grew ever thicker.

On the third day the stranger began to turn yellow. By midday his face was as green as grass. That whole day the captain was the only one who spoke. Nothing seemed to bother him. His face was slightly redder than usual, but that was all.

"No, no, no!" the stranger called out suddenly, and he fell over flat on his back. The fall pushed his top hat off, and two little horns peeped out.

"I see!" said Captain Van Hunks when he saw them. "So you were the Devil all the time."

"Yes," said the Devil, and he got up slowly, "I've come to fetch you."

"But I won!" old Captain Van Hunks protested.

The only answer was a flash of lightning and a clap of thunder. The whole world smelt of sulphur. When the blue fumes cleared, there was a great burnt patch on the mountain to mark the place where old Van Hunks and the Devil had sat. But there was no sign of the two of them.

Two of the old captain's slaves who had gone to find their master, arrived just in time to see what happened. They fled without once looking back, and their story quickly spread through the whole town.

But as the years passed, the story grew. Old Van Hunks was such a pigheaded fellow, people said, that even the Devil could not get the better of him. He kept on nagging the Devil that he had been tricked by him, and that he had won the smoking competition. When things got too bad, the Devil brought him

back to the Windberg to smoke again, but he could never get the better of old Van Hunks. With pipe and tobacco he was the champion.

The Cape has changed since that first competition. Sailing ships have gone. Smoking monsters and sleek racehounds of the seven seas use the new harbour now. Captain Van Hunk's little house has turned to dust, and his mountain is now called Devil's Peak.

The people he used to know, have all died long ago. New generations have come and gone. Old Van Hunks is unknown now. Only the Devil has his acquaintances in every age.

Nowadays, when Captain Van Hunks and the Devil light their pipes and send the white clouds over the mountain, people say, "Look, Table Mountain has its tablecloth on again. The south-easter will blow." Then they pull their doors shut and close the windows fast, not knowing that if you screw up your eyes, you can see the two old smokers' pipes glowing high against the side of Devil's Peak.

The war between the animals and the birds

At the very beginning of things, when you could still fold Table Mountain up in a kaross and when Lion's Head was a cub, the animals were made. And when the making was finished, one and all took the road to the plains. First they had to find out: how do my feet move? Or: are my wings put on right? When each had discovered how everything belonging to them worked, they looked around at one another. Then there was a real commotion.

Little Wagtail's tail nowadays still goes up and down from the shock he got that time when he first saw Ostrich behind him. Mole could not abide the teasing of the others, so he stuck his head in the ground and tunnelled far away.

Lynx and Porcupine crept into the dark and never showed their faces again. Lion and Leopard walked off together, for they were proud animals that stood no nonsense. Baboon and Monkey were the only ones who laughed at all the teasing, for they knew: crying only made your eyes go red.

It did not stop at teasing. The game became rough. It came to blows. Hard biting made fur and tail feathers fly. The animals began to choose sides among themselves. The four-footed animals stood more and more to one side, while all the winged ones gathered together. Things went from bad to worse until the birds and insects exclaimed, "No, we've had enough!" and they flew away to work out a plan and sharpen their stings.

But Jackal Longhead saw what was going on. He called to the other four-footed animals, "Here comes trouble! The flying creatures will make a surprise attack. Choose me as captain so that we can sort things out."

Old Wolf threw his weight against it, but the rest of the

43

animals shouted him down, "Yes, yes! Jackal's our captain! What must we do, Captain Jackal?"

"First we must send out a spy," said Jackal. The animals were content. This captain obviously knew how to fight a battle. "Fieldmouse," he called, "your coat is the colour of the grass and bush, and your nose is sharp. Go to the winged ones and sniff out what there is to be sniffed out."

"Fine, Captain," said Spy Fieldmouse, and he made tracks.

Jackal then climbed onto the biggest rock and surveyed his soldiers. "Four-feet," said he, "remember, this is war. Fight with teeth and claw! Fight with horn and hoof! The enemy is numerous, but that's not enough. We'll show them!"

"That's telling them, Captain!" shouted the animals, each in their own voice. Lion coughed umph-umph, Duiker bleated, and Porcupine shook his quills so that they rattled together clack, clack, clack!

"When the battle begins, I'll take my stand on the highest hill," Jackal said cautiously. "I'll hold my tail in the air. Keep an eye on me. As long as things are going well with us, the flag will fly high. If I drop it, you'll know that we're beaten."

While the four-footed animals were talking, the winged ones were not idle. Honeybee's sting was honed so sharp that he cut his own front leg with it. Mosquito was chewing nettles to sharpen his bite still further. Grasswarbler, the Tiny One,

darted here and there
from the one to the
other, making sure
that everything was
ready. He was the fly-
ing animals' captain.
He could get through
where another would be held
back, and he could creep in
where no other would dare to
go – and this, they reckoned,
was how a leader should be.

Suddenly Hawk shot into
the bushes and reappeared with Fieldmouse
in his beak. Goodness, the winged ones nearly had fits. Hen clean swallowed her words,
and to this very day she is struggling to get out
the "C . . . c . . . come" of "Come and look!" Sparrow got into
such a rage that he nearly fell off his branch:

Death and destruction
Wherever you go!
Here is a sneak
Spying for our foe.

Even today you can still hear him babbling in the treetops as
he tells of the spy they caught that day. He obviously has a bad
memory, because he says now that it was he who gripped
Fieldmouse in his beak and brought him to Captain
Grasswarbler.

Owl hooted, "Hoo . . . hoo . . ." but before he could get out
his "Who on earth," the captain said, "Now, Owl, you've got the
biggest eyes. Take the spy and guard him." Owl shut Fieldmouse
in a crevice in a rock and sat at the mouth. "Hoo . . . hoo . . ."
he tried again – and he is still trying today.

Now there was nothing to stop them. "Attack, my winged ones!" screamed Grasswarbler, and he shot into the air.

The four-footed animals were still waiting for news from their spy when the winged creatures dropped from the sky. "Attack, feet!" shouted Jackal, and he made off for the nearest mound. There he stood at ease, with his tail in the air, watching the battle.

Below on the plain the fighting was furious. Amid the yelping and buzzing and roaring and hissing, confusion reigned. Wave upon wave of winged creatures dived down, but the four-footed animals stood fast. Of all the flyers, only Ostrich had any effect. He kicked open a path with his big feet until Donkey Hit-the-Mark got at him. And when the animals looked over their shoulders and saw Jackal's flag still flying, they attacked again in force. It seemed as if the winged creatures would have to give ground.

Then something moved in the grass, stealthily slipping, quietly listening, looking behind, moving ahead, quickly slithering through the drift, hiding and sliding behind a thorn bush. Yes, it was Wolf. He had never forgiven Jackal for becoming the leader, and he

meant to betray him. Just nearby Pipit was sitting, resting on a branch before he returned to try again, though with his small beak and slender feet he could not do much damage. His wings hung down, he gasped for breath, and he was even greyer than usual.

"Pipit," said Wolf softly, "where's your captain?"

Pipit jumped. "That I won't tell you," he answered boldly.

"You're going to lose the battle," said Wolf. "I could tell you how you can win."

Pipit thought this over for a while, but he did not have the brains for such things. Perhaps he had better call Grasswarbler. "Wait a bit," he said. He slipped here, and he slipped there between the fighters until he found the captain. He brought him back to the thorn bush.

"What is it?" Grasswarbler said bluntly when he saw Wolf. He did not like traitors, but what could he do?

Wolf spoke straight to the point. "Is that so?" said Grasswarbler when he heard the story about Jackal's tail. "We shall soon find an answer for that."

He whizzed off to look for Honeybee. Bee's sting was hot from all the hard work, but it was still as sharp as nails.

"Hit Jackal under the tail," ordered Grasswarbler.

"Fine, Captain," said Bee, and he was gone.

When he got at Jackal the first time, the flag quivered. "Ouch!" yelped the captain, looking round.

At the second sting, the flag sank low. "Ouch, ouch!" shrieked Jackal and danced about.

The third sting was the deathblow. "Ou-ou-ouch!" howled Captain Jackal, and he fled over the hill – helter-skelter, head over heels, grazing and scraping his bottom on the stones, tail between his legs. Even today he would rather drag his tail than lift it up.

The four-footed animals were shocked when they saw that Jackal's flag no longer flew.

"It's all up with us!" one groaned.

"A whole commando of ostriches is coming!" yelled another.

They turned and fled. Hare was well ahead, with Wild Dog close on his heels; that is why these two are still so fast today. Some just dived into the river; that is why some animals still live in the water. Some climbed trees. Some dug holes. That day the four-footed animals learnt many things that they would rather not have known.

And the flying creatures? Some found out how to eat meat. Mosquito hunted so happily that even today he cannot stop. Others dived into the river to get at the fleeing animals. Today we still see how much birds love to romp in water.

Very soon the flying creatures were exhausted with fighting, and the four-footed animals were dead beat with running. "That's enough," called Captain Grasswarbler, and the winged creatures did not argue.

Now the world was in confusion. Wounded creatures of all kinds lay everywhere. Something had to be done.

Jackal was the animal's doctor. Baboon and monkey helped him. But they were much too careless. Where there was a cut, they closed it up – no matter how. Where there was a hole, they patched it – no matter with what. They covered the open cuts on the necks of Horse and Donkey with pieces of tail skin, so they ended up with manes. Springbuck boasted a white rag over his chest, and a white cloth over his whole stomach. They pulled the pieces of skin on the throats of Ox and Cow together holus-bolus, so that even today they hang loose. The animals got spots and stripes, but Jackal and his helpers were too hurried to bother.

Crocodile was the armourer. Everyone who wanted to be protected in case the birds and insects ever attacked again, went to him. Anteater, Lizard, and Cape Monitor stood in the queue. Quickly Crocodile cut a few ox horns in pieces and stuck them onto their bodies. Tortoise got a whole house that from then on he took with him everywhere.

Hawk patched up the winged ones. His grey coat was still neat, for he had let no one rough him up. So he could help the others. The poor things were in a bad way, but Hawk pressed on with his work. He pulled a white shirt onto Crow. Peacock got a tail like a patchwork quilt. Old Parrot also emerged rather gaily coloured. But do not imagine that they cared. Oh no! They were very proud of Hawk's efforts. When he came to repairing their beaks, one could really see some spectacular things: just look at what Bushveld Crow got, not to speak of Hornbill!

But when they had finished the patching and darning, the time came to settle accounts. Why had Jackal fled? Well, he had all sorts of excuses, but the four-footed animals would not swallow any of them. He was immediately dismissed as their leader. And Wolf? Plotting cannot be hidden. Not one of them could prove anything, but there was suspicion – and from that day on Jackal gave old Wolf no rest.

The flying creatures met to deal with Fieldmouse, the spy. But what was happening there? Owl sat in front of the crevice, murmuring, "Hoo . . . hoo . . . hoo?" to himself.

"Where's Fieldmouse, Owl?"

Owl jumped. Well, Fieldmouse was there a little time ago, but now he did not know.

He should not have said that.

"Hey, hey!" crowed Crow.

"Look out, you!" threatened Cuckoo.

"What on earth have you done?" scolded Babbler.

"Get him, wings!" ordered Grasswarbler.

Left and right,
Serves him right!
You peck here,
I'll claw there.
Confusion reigns
In the air.

51

The flying creatures rushed so higgledy-piggledy to get at Owl that he slipped out from under their claws. Then he had to find a way to escape. He crept into a dark hole, and even to this day he does not dare show his face in daylight.

Of course he was furious with Fieldmouse over the trouble he had got him into, so that is why he hunts Fieldmouse whenever he sees him.

The birds were still not at all pleased with the way things had turned out. They turned on Grasswarbler.

"You made Owl the sentry," they said. "You're a rotten leader."

And there and then they gave him his marching orders.

52

How the animals chose a king

A great discussion was going on among the animals of the veld. They wanted a king. How about Lion? He was big and strong.

"Oh no!" said Jackal when he heard this. "We must have a king with horns as well as fangs."

Fangs and horns! That would indeed be a king in a thousand.

That evening Jackal was up to his usual tricks. He searched for the horns of a dead buck, and he stole some bee glue.

When the animals gathered again the next morning, who should march over the rise but Jackal, the Horned Beast. He had stuck

the horns to his head with the bee glue. From far off he proclaimed in a deep voice:

Above, below,
Fangs show in a row,
Horns spread wide
On either side.

"Yes, yes, this is our king!" the animals shouted when they saw him. "Look at his fangs and horns!"

Full of himself, Jackal swaggered among them and ordered them here and there. It was, "Go there!" and they went; "Come here!" and they came. He dragged Lion around by the whiskers and Lion could do nothing, for this was the king's work.

But the sun cooked Jackal's goose. Just as he was lording it over Lion, the bee glue began to melt. When he nodded his head again, the horns lay on the ground.

"You cheat!" roared Lion. He caught Jackal a glancing blow down his back, for now it was Jackal's turn to make tracks.

That was the day when Lion became king. And as for Jackal, even now you can see the grey stripe down his back where Lion's claw caught him.

How the birds and the insects fell out

It happened one day that strife arose among the winged creatures. After the birds and the insects had fought the four-footed animals so successfully, they began to pick quarrels with each other. The birds became particularly ill-mannered, because they were so much bigger than the insects.

"We're going to court about this," declared the insects.

"Fine!" said the birds, and they appointed their own judges. The chief justice was Parrot. Butcherbird and Crow sat with him. Secretarybird wrote down all that was said so that no one could twist his words later on. The other birds crowded on the branches to enjoy themselves, for none of them took the insects' complaints seriously.

The insects began. The first to speak was Grasshopper, but his voice was so squeaky that the judges could not hear a word.

"Louder!" screamed Crow.

Bee tried next, but he buzzed so loudly through his nose that no one could make out what he wanted to say.

"Speak up!" shrieked Butcherbird.

"Listen!" shouted Cicada and Cricket, and the two of them

started speaking together. The noise was deafening. The birds' ears rang.

"For goodness sake!" groaned Parrot:

Beetle, Beetle, clicker-clack:
Speak softer, or I'll break your back!

The birds chattered and crowed with laughter. But the insects did not find it funny at all. Cicada was not at a loss for words, and he answered:

Daddy Polly, best beware,
Or I'll strip your feathers bare!

One word led to another; rude words and ruder laughter. And the longer the argument went on, the stronger the words became, until Horsefly shouted, "The birds are looking for a fight. Insects, let's give them something to think about!"

The rumpus was something that is not often seen. The birds stabbed the insects with their beaks, pecking, tearing and smashing till feelers and wing-cases were flying about every-where. Some insects crept away under stones, and some into cracks, and even today they still live there. Many never flew again. Many still look the worse for wear, just as they did after the birds had beaten them up.

But there were insects that fought back. Horsefly was a dangerous customer. Just have a look at the many bumps that still swell some birds' heads. Secretarybird hid his pens behind his ears, and he has never been able to get them out again.

To this day most birds eat insects. The two species still make things as difficult for each other as they can.

How the birds chose a king

When the birds heard that the animals had chosen a king, they decided to select one as well. But how and whom? That was the problem.

Grasswarbler had a plan as usual. "The power of a bird lies in his wings," he declared. "Therefore the bird who flies the highest, shall be our king."

"Yes, for sure," said Vulture and Eagle. The other birds agreed too, for each was sure that he was the best flyer of them all.

The next morning everything that called itself a bird turned up. Grasswarbler made them all stand in a long row, but he took care that he was near Eagle. "One, two, three!" he counted. Then he slipped under one of Eagle's wings and happily rode up with him on a quill feather.

The birds put out all their strength. Old Guineafowl and Partridge did not get very high before their wings gave in, and they fell down plump on their bottoms. Some birds turned back when they reached the clouds, and they got off unscathed. Others pushed on heavenwards, and today they are still burnt

bald. Ostrich's big body told against him, but he held out. His
neck was burnt bare, and his feathers withered. When he fell,
he broke all except two of the toes on each foot. From that time
onwards he did not want to fly any more.

Finally only Eagle and Vulture remained in the contest to
settle the matter. High is high, but it was amazing how those
two birds flew. First one was on top, then the other one slipped
past him. Grasswarbler sat and watched the whole affair from
Eagle's wing feather. Never before in his life had he been so
high above the earth. Every so often he lifted his wings a little
bit so that the cool wind could ruffle his breast feathers.

58

Finally Vulture groaned, "I can go no higher."

"I can," said Eagle, and he shot past him.

"Then you're the king," said Vulture.

"Thank you," said Eagle.

But Grasswarbler flew silently out from under Eagle's wing and circled above his head. "Dippety-do! Dippety-do!" he called. "I'm the highest. Now I'm the king of the birds!"

Eagle thought his ears had tricked him, but seeing was believing. "I can go higher yet," he said and set off. Again Grasswarbler rested on his quill feather until Eagle called out, "How are things now, my friend?"

"Dippety-do!" called out Grasswarbler from above his head. "Still fine."

"I'll show you!" said Eagle, and Grasswarbler hitched another lift. Eagle's breath now came in gasps, and his wings felt as if they were being torn from his body. "Where are you now, little one?" he groaned.

For the third time Grasswarbler dived out from under his wing and sang out above his head, "Dippety-do! Dippety-do! I am king. I've flown the highest."

"Yes," said Eagle, "you are king. I can go no higher."

When they came back to earth, all the birds spoke at once, as they love to do. Each wanted to be the first to know, "Who won? Vulture or eagle?"

"Neither," sighed Eagle, "it's Grasswarbler," And Vulture agreed.

"What?" shrieked the birds. "We won't have such a whipper-snapper for a king. Kill him! Kill him!"

If Grasswarbler had not been so nimble on the wing, they would have torn him to pieces then and there. But he saw trouble coming and dived into a mouse hole. There he sat, where no one could get at him.

"He'll get hungry and thirsty," said Parrot. "Let's set a guard at the hole to catch him when he comes out. What about Butcherbird? He's wide awake and alert."

"Yes," agreed the birds, "Butcherbird will guard him." Then they flew off to look for food, for they were all hungry after the day's doings.

The sun got hot, but Grasswarbler sat. Midday came, and he still had not moved a foot. Evening crept out of the ravines, but Grasswarbler held out.

Butcherbird's stomach screamed with hunger, for he had a good appetite. "Come now," he said to himself, "Grasswarbler must be so weak from lack of food and water that he won't be able to move. I'll just fly out for a while to snatch a bite."

But Butcherbird had hardly turned his back before Grasswarbler slipped out.

"How's this?" asked the birds when they saw Grasswarbler fluttering in the trees.

Butcherbird had to make his report. "Grasswarbler's still in the hole," he said.

"No, he's not," said the birds.

"Yes, he is," said Butcherbird furiously.

"Look for yourself, there on the branch," said the birds.

"What on earth . . .!" said Butcherbird when he saw Grasswarbler. "Now how did that happen?"

"That's what we want to know from you," said the birds.

"I have no idea," answered Butcherbird.

"I can't believe my own ears. Now I'll never say another word!" declared Egyptian Vulture, and from that day on he has never made a sound.

The birds now were after Butcherbird's blood, but he was a dangerous fighter, and they thought better of it. Even today no bird is fond of him, while Butcherbird is still trying to get at Grasswarbler. That is why he hangs all the little birds he can get his claws on, hoping that one of them will be the culprit.

So it happened that even today the birds have no king. Only Grasswarbler sometimes circles above the bushes when Butcherbird is far away and mocks the lot of them, "Dippety-do! I'm king! I'm king!"

The mouse who was too clever

Snake lived in an oak forest. He lived well too. Nearby was a large colony of mice, and Snake loved mice.

Every morning, just as the sun's red face peered over the mountain, Snake unwound himself from the coil in which he had slept that night. "Now, how about catching another mouse?" he said to himself, licking his cold, black lips with his thin, red tongue.

Quickly he slid through the long grass. His body glistened in the sun, for he was as fat as butter. At the mouse runway he lay still as death and waited.

It was not long before a mouse came running

along the track to look for food in the grass. Snake reared up and hissed: not too softly, or the mouse would not hear; not too loudly, or else the mouse would be frightened and run off. He hissed just loud enough. The mouse looked up inquisitively – right into Snake's eyes. When he saw his old enemy right in front of him, he was so terrified that he stood stock-still. Slowly Snake advanced, then struck like lightning. The mouse had barely time to give three squeaks before he vanished down Snake's gullet.

But there was one mouse whom Snake could not catch. When this mouse came down the track, Snake reached up as always and hissed just right. But this mouse did not stop. He whisked into the grass and, with one squeak, was gone. What angered Snake most was that the squeak sounded just like a laugh.

One day, as Mouse came happily down the trail, Snake could bear it no longer. Instead of hissing, he called as amiably as he could, "Mouse, listen to me for a bit."

Mouse stood dead still and gave three squeaks. Now Snake was sure: Mouse was laughing! Snake swallowed his rage and continued, "I just want to ask, my dear Mouse, how you always manage to escape me?"

"I'm too clever for you," Mouse answered boldly. He sat back on his hind legs to curl his moustache.

"It seems so," said Snake, acting humble. "Won't you tell me how you manage it?"

"It's simple if you've got brains," said Mouse.

63

"Yes?" inquired Snake.

"I just don't look into your eyes when you hiss. Then you're powerless!" said Mouse.

"Oh no, Mouse, it can't be that simple," Snake said, pretending to be angry. "I think it's fright that makes you run so fast."

"No!" declared Mouse.

"Oh yes!" said Snake.

"No!"

"Yes!"

"No!"

"All right then, look into my eyes so that I can see if you speak the truth," said Snake.

"Fine! I'll look!" Mouse said angrily.

For the first time he stared into Snake's eyes, and Snake, without moving an inch, looked right into his. Mouse wanted to say something, but he was silent. Too late he realised that Snake had outwitted him.

Slowly Snake swung his head from side to side. Mouse's head swung too. Nearer and nearer Snake came, but Mouse sat stone-still. When Snake struck and caught him, Mouse had not even the strength to squeak.

Snake slithered away to warm in the sun, content at last. All that remained of the clever mouse was a bulge in Snake's throat.

The great thrist
A San tale

Far, far back, when Kaggen, the mantis, made the animals, there were no springs or rivers or waterholes on earth. All the animals had to drink was each other's blood, and they ate the meat off each other's bones. Those were bloody days, and no living thing was safe.

Then Elephant, the Great One, he who could see over the hills to the faraway places, said, "This cannot go on. I would rather be dead. Then my bones could become fruit trees, and my sinews could trail across the ground and bear wild melons, and my hair could become a grassy plain."

And the animals asked, "How long must we wait, Elephant? How long must we wait? For you come of a long-lived race."

"I do not know," said Elephant. "We must see."

But Snake said, "I'll help you!" And before Elephant

could move a foot, Snake struck deeply with his poisoned fangs, and he did not withdraw them till Elephant lay dead on the ground.

The animals fell upon the carcass: Lion and Leopard, Jackal and Hare, and old Tortoise with his bandy legs. They ate and

ate the meat from Elephant's body, and they lapped up his blood. They stopped only when all that was left were his bones and sinews and hair. Then they went to sleep, for they had all eaten their fill.

But when they woke the next day, they began to complain again. They said, "Elephant is now dead and eaten. What are we going to live on?" They would surely have cried if there had been tears, but the sun drank their bodies dry, and their eyes remained dull.

"You must wait," said Snake. "Elephant promised."

"Elephant promised if he died on his own," said the animals, "but you killed him."

"Don't despair yet," said Snake. "Let's not be too hasty. Wait and see. Or will one of you try to drink my blood?"

All the animals were afraid of his poisoned fangs and they kept quiet.

That night when the stars rose one by one from their resting places, a new light burnt in the heavens. "It's Elephant's spirit!" said the frightened animals. "Now he'll surely come to kill us all."

"Wait and see!" said Snake.

Elephant's eyes were two bright blazes in the sky, which climbed ever higher until they hung right over the place where the animals had torn him to pieces. Then he must have said something that the animals could not hear, for suddenly his bones rose upright, and they put down roots and grew branches heavy with fruit. His sinews spread over the earth, and his hair became grass on the plain.

"Now we have food!" the animals rejoiced and began to graze. But some of them could not do without flesh and blood. Therefore they crept away in the darkness: Lion and Leopard, Jackal and Wolf, Wildcat and Owl. When the other animals went to sleep, they came out to kill and rend. Hawk was so bold that he sought his prey in broad daylight. Only Vulture declared, "I also want meat, but I will not kill."

Yet even now that they had food, the animals were not satisfied. "Water, water!" they moaned. "We're dying of thirst."

"The fruit's full of water," said Snake, "and the wild melons."

"Water, water, water!" groaned the animals, and they looked at one another to see whose young blood would be best to drink.

"Elephant gave you his body," Snake angrily declared, "and I gave you my poison. Yet you aren't satisfied." The animals did not know it, but Elephant was so big that Snake had used all his venom to kill him. "I'll give you water too."

Snake disappeared into a hole in the earth. He hissed and blew and spat great jets of water until it bubbled out of the ground and rushed down the gullies and filled the wastes.

"Now we have a fountain and rivers and waterholes," rejoiced the animals, and they were satisfied.

That is how the animals got food and water, and that is why, even today, we still speak of elephant grass and the water-snake.

The watersnake
A San tale

Deep down where the fountain rose, bubbling up through the reeds, where it was always cool, lived Watersnake. She was the daughter of the waters. Her body glistened and her eyes were bright, but brightest of all was the great white stone on her head. She had found it deep in the earth, and she guarded it jealously. When she swam down the river, sending ripples against the banks, she carried it high in the sun. But when she drank, she hid it first in the long reeds, for she feared that it would fall off and be lost. If she sensed that someone wanted

to steal it, then, like the wind and the lightning, she was upon him to rend him or squeeze him to death. But whoever could steal it would gain huge wealth and happiness.

Once upon a time there was a young man of the veld who had heard much talk of Watersnake and her stone. "I must have it," he said to himself. Day after day he hid near the spring and waited till Watersnake went past. He had to narrow his eyes and peer through the slits, for the stone shone like the sun and would blind anyone who looked straight at it. Each day Watersnake disappeared round the bend with the stone still on her head, but each day the young man waited lower down, until he found the clump of reeds in which she always hid it.

The following day he came early and covered himself with grass and bushes, hoping that Watersnake would not know he was there and would hide the stone as usual. She had scarcely turned to drink, before the young man crept nearer. He threw a kaross over the glittering stone so that it would not blind his eyes and slithered away on his stomach over the rise. Then he ran till he was out of danger and buried it under a rock.

Strange things started happening to him. Before, he had been just another man. Now, everyone wanted to be his friend. They hastened to bring him gifts, and he became rich and happy. Only in the evenings, when the wind blew from the river, and he heard Watersnake weeping, he became restless.

Every day he went to the river to see how Watersnake was doing. Her skin shone no more, and her eyes were dull. But she did more than mourn. She wanted her stone back, and she sought help. First she asked Crocodile, "Do you know who stole my stone?"

"I saw something brown move among the reeds," he answered.

The next day, when Jackal came to drink, Watersnake stopped him. "Do you know something brown that stole my stone from the reeds?" she asked.

"I saw his tracks over the rise," he answered. "It was a two-legged animal."

A few evenings later Hare was feeding beside the river. "Do you know who took my stone from among the long reeds?" she asked. "It was a brown animal that walked on two legs."

"I saw him running like the wind," answered Hare, "with a kaross in his hand."

Then Watersnake knew that it was the deed of one of the men of the veld. She became so angry that she drank the whole river dry. When she slid through the veld towards the hunters' fires, the water rumbled like thunder inside her.

But the young man had heard how she had questioned the animals and how she had got onto his trail. That very day, at noon, he had taken the stone back quietly and hidden it again among the reeds.

"Flee, everyone!" called out the men when Watersnake's head appeared out of the dark with lightning flashing in her eyes.

"No, let's hear if we can perhaps help her," said the young man.

"I'm looking for my stone," hissed Watersnake. "One of you took it."

"Who says that?" asked the young man.

"Crocodile saw," she said, "and Jackal and Hare."

"Crocodile's a rogue," said the young man. "Jackal's a beggar. Hare can't even deliver a message properly."

Watersnake knew that he spoke the truth. Her head sank low. Her sighs were a stormy wind among the bushes, and the earth shook under her tears.

"Do not weep, Watersnake," said the young man. "Do not sigh. Let's go back and search again. Perhaps you didn't look properly."

Then he went with her to the reeds, and he pulled out the stone from where he had hidden it at midday, and he gave it to her – but he was careful not to look at it.

Through the night, the men round the fire heard a sound like the song of many rivers, but there were no clouds in the sky. Then they knew it was Watersnake laughing. When the young man came back, they all shouted, "He's the wisest and the best man that ever was. Watersnake had lost her stone, and he recovered it. Watersnake was angry, but he gave her peace. Watersnake was heartbroken, but he made her laugh again!" While the ashes grew cold and the moon went to sleep, they danced the Dance of the Young Man and the Watersnake, and they loaded the young man with so many gifts that he did not know what to do with them all.

So he remained rich and happy, even though he did not possess the stone any more. The river ran again, the ripples broke on the banks, and the sun flashed on Watersnake as she swam round the bend with the great white stone on her head.

Little Hare Harelip
A San tale

Mother Full Moon peered over the shoulder of the mountain at the people on the plain. She saw how they rejoiced at her coming. She saw them dance. But she knew that all men carry a stone in their hearts, for they feared death.

"I must send a message to my children," she said to herself. "Then they will never again be unhappy." She searched with shining eyes through the night until she saw Owl, who was out hunting.

"Owl!" she called. "Will you take a message for me?"

"I cannot," sighed Owl. "The night is short, and mice are few. Leave me alone! Leave me alone!"

"Now I understand why you always have to hide in the dark," said Mother Full Moon with disgust. "There is no light or warmth in your heart."

Just then, trotting around a bush, came Jackal, sniffle-snuffling here and there and everywhere, smelling out stuff no one else wanted, so that he could eat it.

"Jackal!" called Mother Full Moon. "Will you take a message for me?"

Jackal sat on his haunches, stuck his nose in the air and howled, "Oow! Oow! Mother Full Moon, look how I suffer. Look how little I have to live on. Do not ask more of me. Rather help me, help me. Give me food."

"Be off, you beggar!" said Full Moon crossly.

Then she saw Hare feeding in the *uintjie* field. "Hare, will you take a message for me?"

"Yes, yes, Mother Full Moon," he said. He sat bolt upright on his short tail and sang:

I am Hare Four-Foot,
I am Hare-Run-Wild,
I am Hare Fleet-Foot,
I am the Wind's own child.

"I want to send you to my people," said Full Moon, "to the men of the veld."

"I know them, Mother," said Hare.

Mother Full Moon continued, "You must tell them this: Look at Mother Moon, and be content. First she is like the horn of an eland. Then she becomes round and fat like the hunters when the herds of animals are plentiful, and every arrow finds its mark. Then she melts away until there is only a crane's wishbone left. In the end she vanishes completely. So it is with men too. First a man is young, and he grows strong. Then comes old age and sucks his bones dry. But when he dies, he shall live again – just as I do."

"Is that all, Mother?" asked Hare.

"Yes, but . . ." said Full Moon. Before she could say, "Wait a while!" Hare had gone. He ran so fast that the stones went flying behind him, and the bushes rustled. He ran and sang:

I am Hare Four-Foot,
I am Hare-Run-Wild,
I am Hare Fleet-Foot,
I am the Wind's own child.

Whoops! He crashed so hard into something that he had to sit back on his hind legs.

"Can't you look where you're going?" asked the thing. It was a man of the veld.

"I was looking for you," said Hare importantly. "Mother Full Moon sent me. She says you are Eland's horn. No, she says you are Crane's wishbone. I mean, she says, when you are dead, you're dead, and you won't live again."

"Yes," sighed the man, and he hung his head. This was what he had always feared.

"Perhaps it's the other way round!" Hare called after him, for he was completely muddled by now, but the man was already gone.

Hare hung his head. He peered over his shoulder and saw Mother Full Moon's face, red above the mountains. She looked full of anger.

Hare slipped under a bush. He ran through the dark places to his lair. But Mother Full Moon lay in wait for him. When he came around a high tussock of grass, she grabbed him by the hind leg.

"Bad one!" said Mother Full Moon. "You bungled everything!"

"But, Mother . . ." began Hare. Before he could say, "Full Moon" she smacked him in the face so violently that his lip split open.

"You will have a harelip for ever, because you did not listen carefully to what I told you!" said Mother Full Moon.

"Yes, Mother," said Hare, "but how can I put right the mess I made?"

Then Mother Full Moon's heart melted. "Go," she said, "go quickly, and give my people the right message."

The envious lions

Lion and his two brothers had a grievance. The trouble lay with their young wives. If you listened to them, everyone and everything was stronger and cleverer and much better than their young husbands. And when their husbands tried anything to prove them wrong, they just laughed.

Take Monkey, look how nimble he was! Gemsbuck, see him run! And as for Ostrich! When it came to roaring, well, the lion brothers might as well keep quiet – so their wives said.

"We've got to do something," said Lion, and his brothers agreed. They decided to invite all the animals to a big party. Then they would show their young wives who the real kings were.

At midday the guests started to arrive, one by one. Monkey was first, swinging up and down through the trees, somersaulting, light-footed on the ground. "Look at him," said the wives loudly. "Monkey is quite the most nimble animal!"

"Come, let's dance," said Lion sulkily. They began, but when the lions swung their great hindquarters and lumbered round in a circle, their wives shrieked with laughter. Monkey floated over the earth, front leg, hind leg, front leg, hind leg, whipping around. He danced Lion and his brothers into the ground.

"Monkey has won!" screamed the wives. "When Monkey starts dancing, our husbands might as well go to sleep."

Then Gemsbuck came, proudly parading his long, thin legs. "What a beauty!" said the wives, and they had eyes only for him.

Lion had no more desire to dance. "Come, let's have a race," he said, and they set off. The lions kept up for the first few bounds, then Gemsbuck ran so fast that they could only stand and stare.

"Good for you, Gemsbuck!" called the lion wives. "You're too fast for our husbands."

Over the hill then came Ostrich, bellowing. Lion did not even try to open his mouth, for the womenfolk were so besotted with Ostrich's beautiful voice that they heard nothing else.

"We'd better be off, brothers," said Lion. "There's nothing we can do here." They went away through the bushes, leaving their wives in ecstasies.

But they did not go far. They settled in a cave on the side of the mountain, and they caught monkeys to become more nimble, gemsbuck to become faster runners, and ostriches so that they could roar more deeply.

At first their wives found their departure a big joke. But on the second and third day they had difficulty in finding food. By the

79

fourth day their children had become uncontrollable. On the fifth day the lion wives were sad at heart. They said to one another, "We must go and get our husbands back. They really are the best of all the animals." And they did.

From that time on, no lion wife praises any other animal, for she is afraid that her husband will leave her.

Get him, Jackal!
I. Hare's horse

Jackal was annoyed with Hare who had been telling Jackal's wife tales behind Jackal's back. Now she would not have her husband in the house. But Hare had many tricks up his sleeve. One day when he heard Jackal trotting quietly down the path, he lay down in the bushes and groaned.

"Ha! Now I've got you," said Jackal, ready to pounce.

Hare answered in a weak voice, "Take me, Jackal. I'm too sick to run away. Please put me on your back and carry me to your house."

This was not such a bad idea, thought Jackal. His wife would be only too pleased with him if he arrived with a nice piece of hare for dinner. Helter-skelter Jackal set off along the path. Hare had to hold on for dear life.

"Jackal!" he called after a while. "The flies are bothering me. Please pick me a cane switch so that I can chase them off."

"You've got a nerve, Hare!" said Jackal, but he gave him a switch.

When they were still a good way from Jackal's house, his wife came out onto the verandah to see what her husband was doing there.

"Wife, Wife!" called Jackal, "I've brought you a nice, fat hare."

But look what happened then: Hare was no longer half dead with pain. He sat straight up and used the cane switch as a whip. "Wife, Wife!" he called, mimicking Jackal, "I've brought you a nice, fat jackal." The whip hissed over Jackal's shoulders – he gave a great bound, and pranced and galloped. Hare shot off Jackal's back and disappeared, laughing, into the undergrowth.

"Whoever heard of a jackal letting himself be ridden by a hare!" cried out Jackal's wife. "Such a sorry fool is not for me. Get out of my sight!"

2. The church of the bees

Hare was running up the mountainside, when he came upon a bees' nest deep in a crevice in the rock. "So ho!" murmured hare:

Sweet is sweet,
And a treat to eat.
The best for me,
Comes from a bee.

Hare pushed his head deep into the crevice to get at the nest, not knowing that Jackal was on his track. He still had his head inside, when Jackal grabbed him by the heel.

"Aha! Now I've got you, Hare," said Jackal, ready to give his teeth some exercise. But Hare quickly got over his fright and had a plan handy. "Hush, Jackal," said he, "can't you hear that my friends are at church?"

"Where?" asked Jackal, always inquisitive.

"Here in the crevice. Don't they sing beautifully?"

"Let me hear," said Jackal and stuck his head in, but he pulled it out immediately again, saying, "Sing? Surely you don't call that singing – It's just buzz-buzz-buzz, all on one note."

"They must be tired," said Hare. "Give them a bit of a poke with a stick, in there through their front door, so they can know we're here. Then you'll hear."

Jackal grabbed a stick and pottered about with it in the crevice. The he stuck his head in to listen.

It was wicked, what happened next. The bees gave Jackal a thorough going-over; they wrecked him; they stung him nearly to death. He jumped up and ran, but the bees kept at him. It was zoom-ping! "Ouch!" Zoom-ping! Zoom-ping! Zoom-ping! "Ouch! Ouch! Ouch!"

Hare fell over, laughing. He roared with laughter until his sides ached. Jackal would not worry him again in a hurry, oh no!

3. Get him, Jackal!

But Hare was altogether too pleased with himself. Down the path he went, singing, hop-skipping over the bushes. Not looking where he was going, not going where he was looking, and whoops! – there he sat on his bottom. Jackal had spread birdlime on a log and had put it down in the pathway. Hare struggled, but only stuck faster. He tugged and lugged, he pushed and pulled and shouted.

Jackal came out from behind the bushes. "Aha! Now I've got you," he said. His lips were still swollen all skew with the bee stings, so that he seemed to be laughing.

Hare became very quiet. "Yes, you've caught me, Jackal," he said. "Now you can eat me. I'm only sorry that I have to die when I'm thirsty. I was just going to the river."

"Well, let's go and have a drink," said Jackal. He had run himself dry getting the trap ready for Hare. He pulled Hare out of the birdlime, threw him over his shoulder and set off for the drinking place.

How still and shining the water lay. Jackal stooped down to drink. But look at this rude fellow! Another jackal had pushed his snout in front of him.

"Move over," growled Jackal.

"What's the trouble?" asked Hare over his shoulder.

"Look for yourself," said Jackal and put him down. "Stand aside!" he said to that other jackal that was still waiting there, looking at him.

Hare saw at once that Jackal was quarrelling with his own reflection, but he said nothing.

"Away with you!" said Jackal for the third time, and he bared his teeth, but the water jackal snarled back.

"Don't let him make fun of you!" Hare egged him on. "Look at his mouth! He's laughing at you. Get him, Jackal!"

When Jackal snapped, the other jackal snapped too. When Jackal pounced, they both landed splash! in the water. When Jackal disappeared, they were both gone.

"Ho, ho, ho!" laughed Hare:

Nasty temper,
Without direction.
Jackal fights
His own reflection.

By the time Jackal had struggled, hangdog, out of the water, Hare was already far up the path, singing his little song.

Soup with a kick
A San tale

(Traditionally the hyena was called a wolf)

Wolf had been on a long journey to visit his brother. Now he was hungry and thirsty. In the veld he came upon Lion, feasting on a zebra. Jackal was sitting close by, waiting for the leftovers.

"Evening, Lion," Wolf said amiably.

"Mmm," said Lion as he cracked open a marrowbone.

Wolf sat back on his haunches. "Well now, are you not going to invite me to a piece of meat?"

"Yes!" said Jackal greedily.

"Keep quiet," said Wolf, and Jackal moved back a few paces.

"No," said Lion, and he tore at the soft flesh of the hindquarters.

"Just a bit of juice to lick up?" asked Wolf. "I'm very thirsty."

"I lick the juices up myself," mumbled Lion.

"Just a marrowbone to chew," begged Wolf.

"There then, take that," said Lion, and he threw Wolf the bone which he had just sucked dry.

"What about me?" whined Jackal.

"Be off!" said Lion, and he raised a paw threateningly.

Jackal shifted even further away.

Wolf took the bone. He chewed on it, as if there were lots to chew on, and he sucked it as if there were lots to suck. Then he stood up.

"Thank you very much, Lion," said he. "I shall not forget such kindness. You're welcome to come tomorrow evening to have some soup with me."

"Thank you, I will," said Lion. He licked his lips at the thought. He knew no one could beat Wolf when it came to making soup.

"Thank you, I will," said Jackal as if Wolf had asked him too. He went to lick at the dry bone that Wolf had left.

Over the next little rise Wolf came upon an ostrich, and he went at him with a will. Feathers and feet flew into the air, and then Wolf tucked in. He dragged the leftover pieces home with him. "You can eat the meat," he said to his wife and children. "Only leave the bones for me."

The next day Wolf put two pots on the fire for the ostrich soup. One he took off in time to get cold, but he kept the other one boiling hot.

It was not long before Lion came along, with Jackal on his tail. "What about that soup you spoke of, Wolf?" asked Lion.

"Yes, what about the soup?" asked Jackal.

"Come and sit in the queue," said Wolf, and he showed them where his wife and children were already waiting.

His wife opened her mouth, and Wolf poured in some soup – from the cold pot. He went from child to child, and they all gulped it down with relish. But when he came to Lion and Jackal, he scooped two mugs full of burning hot soup. "Open wide," he said, and they opened.

He poured it in.

Lion tried to swallow, then he spat it out in a great, steaming rainbow. "Whew! Wolf, my friend," he said, breathlessly, "your soup is vicious today."

"It's made out of ostrich leg," said Wolf. "That bird surely has a tremendous kick. Do you want some more?"

"No, thank you," said Lion. "I think I'll be off now."

And Jackal? He could not swallow, for the soup was too hot. And he could not spit it out, for he was afraid of Wolf. So he just sat there, with tears running down his cheeks. But when Lion loped off, he went to empty his mouth behind a bush. And to this very day when he waits in the moonlight for Lion to finish eating and he thinks of that soup, he cries all over again. Just listen.

"Ho-ot sou-ou-ou-oup," he howls. "O-o-strich sou-ou-oup. Ostrich soup with a kick!"

King Lion's presents

King Lion was giving a party, and all the animals had to attend. A royal invitation was a command that you could not ignore. Only the she-buck were rebellious. "Lion dines far too well on our family," grumbled Kudu's wife. "How do we know he will not eat us at his party?"

"Yes, yes!" agreed the rest of the buck wives.

"Then I must go alone," said Kudu. "Otherwise there's bound to be trouble."

"We'll come too," said the other he-buck.

Only old Goat's wife could not stay away from the prospect of food – even if she was going to be dished up herself.

So the animals arrived at the party: Leopard and Hare, Zebra and Mole, Elephant, Mongoose and Snake. Baboon was too inquisitive to stay away. Donkey was too dense. Rock Rabbit, Hippo and Chameleon came as well. Yes, it was a party in a thousand.

First they danced a while, and Baboon was the star. Then they sang a bit, and Jackal came to the fore. Afterwards they dined on honey and milk. Even Lion, Leopard, Lynx and Wolf joined in as if they had never tasted blood. For Lion had concluded: at a party you cannot dish up your guests' relations.

"Now listen, my animals," said Lion when he had licked the honey pot clean, for a king eats first and last, and sometimes in-between as well. The others had to take what they could get. "Listen, my animals," he repeated, "I wish to give each of you a present to show that I am a good king."

"Thank you!" shouted the animals, and they pressed forward, each afraid that the others would get the best presents.

"Quietly now," ordered Lion. "He who grabs, gets nothing – and the greediest comes last."

Then things went better.

"Those of you who want horns," commanded Lion, "stand to one side."

"Horns?" Kudu asked his friends. "Won't we look good with horns?"

"Yes!" said the buck, and they moved to one side.

"Here you are," said King Lion, and they put them on. "But your wives, who did not come, do not get any."

Elephant saw the buck swaggering off, and he lunged his big body forward. "I also want horns," he demanded, and quickly he grabbed a pair of beautiful white ones with his mouth.

"You greedy thing!" said Lion. "Because you snatched your own present, the horns will stick in your mouth. No carrying them proudly on your head for you!"

"Oh no!" pleaded Elephant. "My nose is too short. I can't . . . I can't . . . I can't breathe!"

"Now you can," said King Lion, and he pulled Elephant's nose until it was nearly hanging on the ground. "Is that better?"

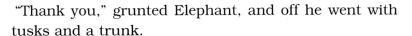

"Thank you," grunted Elephant, and off he went with tusks and a trunk.

But there was more trouble at the pile of horns. Rhinoceros was snuffling around.

"So," growled Lion, "you stick your nose into everything, do you? Well, now your horns will stick to it."

"Nonsense," snorted Rhino, and it looked as though he was going to charge his own king with his nose horns. But Lion gave him such a swipe through his face that one horn broke, and his eyes swelled into slits. That is the reason why Rhino is still so short-sighted, and why his horns are of different sizes.

Lion went up to the next pile. "Beautiful ears here," said he.

But the animals were just like children: they did not have ears, nor did they want any. Lion had picked up two pairs already; and what he took up, he never put down again, for he was the king. "Take these!" he commanded, and he loaded them onto the first two animals that he could reach – Donkey and Hare. They just had to be grateful and thank the king for the gifts.

"Now, those who want fine clothes," said Lion.

There was an uproar. Lion had to keep a cool head, for all the animals longed to show off. Each wished to look more handsome than his neighbour.

Leopard got a spotted suit, and there was a striped jacket for Zebra. Horse and Cow came with long stories.

"We work for Farmer," said Horse.

"We have to be decently dressed every day," went on Cow.

"One suit of clothes is not enough," continued Horse.

"We don't want Farmer to laugh at us animals," ended Cow.

"Agreed, agreed," said Lion, for he approved of Horse's stylish smartness, and Cow's soft voice went straight to his heart. "Here you are."

Horse was first. Fine was not the word! Dapple-grey and chestnut, dark brown and snow-white, and black like midnight itself! "Thank you very much," neighed horse and trotted off. Later on he got tired of changing his clothes every day, and he divided them among his children. That is why each horse has only one suit today, and why horses' suits are so different.

Cow received a spotted dress and a red jacket, and black clothes for Sunday. Later, she also, like Horse, gave the different clothes to her children.

While Lion was still busy with Cow, a voice screamed from the crowd, "Hey, what about me? Don't divide all the best between Horse and Cow!" It was Giraffe.

"Rude one!" roared Lion. "How dare you scream at your king? You won't speak again, ever." And so it happened that Giraffe lost his voice.

Just to show the animals that he would not be rushed, Lion went to the pile of horns and found Cow a set to match each of her dresses.

"Thank you very much," said Cow and went off with her presents.

Giraffe looked so grief-stricken, dumb as he was, that Lion felt sorry for him. "Here's a smart suit for you," said the King, "and a pair of soft horns to go with it."

Giraffe got dressed and cheered up. Lion looked him up and down. "I'll give you a long neck so that you can see your enemies from far," he decided, "and long legs to flee with." Giraffe was very pleased with himself and trotted away happily.

Just as Lion was about to turn back to his task, something moved at his feet. "What now?" he yelled and shot into the air. Before the intruder could get out of the way, Lion landed flat on him. It was Rock Lizard. Out he crept from underneath Lion's claws, with his head black and blue. "That's what you deserve," said the King. "And blue-headed you'll remain!"

By now Lion wanted to get it all over. The sun was hot, and he felt hungry. Milk and honey were really not food for the king of beasts.

The animals had to take what they got. Baboon received a sickle tail, and Rock Rabbit and Mole got long, thin ones. They did not want these presents and secretly buried them, so they ended up with none.

Goat got a beard, and before his wife could blink her eyes, she had one too. The animals sniggered to themselves, but King Lion pressed on. "Next! Next!" he called.

Hippo was landed with four tusks, and Snake, by accident, got Lion's own calabash of herbal medicine that Lion had stolen from a witchdoctor. Snake swallowed the whole lot in one gulp. The stuff began to sizzle, and he had to spit; then it grew into poison, and he started striking at everyone.

"Chop off his legs," Lion shouted, but that did not stop him. Snake was by now so worked up that he slithered away on his stomach, and even today he bites whatever he sees, and his poison is deadly.

Mongoose stole Queen Lion's pot of lavender water and poured the whole lot over himself. Whew! It smelt to high heaven! The animals held their noses and grabbed from the pile what they could: horns, hooves and fantails. Then they took to their heels.

"What about us?" shouted Jackal and Wolf. They had nothing yet, because they were so choosy.

King Lion looked round, tears streaming from his eyes. Only a howl and a laugh remained. "Take it," said Lion, "and don't you dare refuse." The two had to comply. That is why today

Wolf is the one who laughs, and no animal can touch Jackal when it comes to howling.

By the time old Tortoise finally arrived at the place of distribution, all the animals and gifts were gone. This is why he still has the horn shell that Crocodile had made for him. And Frog lives completely naked in the water. He got so warm with all the waiting around that he went quietly off for a swim, but someone stole his clothes. From then on he was too ashamed to appear among the other animals. If he is sitting in the sun and hears something move, he dives away immediately. But at night in the dark he and his brothers come out. Then you can hear them lament. "Where? Where?" complains one. "Clothes! Clothes! Clothes!" complain the others.

Jackal mistrusts his own peace

One day Jackal was snuffling about among a clump of trees, when he spied Cock up on one of the top branches.

"Good morning, my dear cock," Jackal said cordially.

"Good morning," answered Cock. "Where are you off to so early?"

"Just looking for some civil conversation," said Jackal quickly. "But it's not comfortable to talk with one's head held high. Rather come down and sit beside me."

"Not on your life," answered Cock. "I know your tricks, Jackal. If I move any closer, you'll catch me and eat me."

"Never," declared Jackal. "Have you not heard? Peace was declared in Africa between all creatures."

"Coo-coo-le-coo!" laughed Cock.

"What are you laughing at?" asked Jackal.

"At your fine stories," said Cock. "And at my own story too."

"And that is?" asked Jackal.

"Yesterday I was chased by Wild Dog," said Cock, "and I had to fly up into this tree. Now Farmer and his dogs are looking for me. I can see them coming."

"Well, I have to say goodbye." Jackal was suddenly in a hurry.

"Why in such a hurry, Jackal?" asked Cock. "I'm enjoying our little chat. Surely you aren't afraid of the dogs. There's peace in Africa."

"Yes," said Jackal, "but the question is whether those stupid dogs know about it." And he was off.

Jackal the Tiger eater
A Cape Malay tale

(Traditionally a leopard was called a tiger.)

One day Jackal and Tiger slaughtered a young goat. While they were working together, there was peace. But when the goat was hung in the tree and their mouths started to water, they became unfriendly. Each wanted all for himself.

"Thank you," rumbled Tiger, "you can go now."

"Go, my foot," growled Jackal. "What about my share?"

"I caught the goat," said Tiger.

"I cut up most of it," snarled Jackal.

"My knife was blunt," answered Tiger.

"Be careful, or I'll grind your teeth even blunter," threatened Jackal.

"Get out!" roared Tiger.

"You can't make me leave!" scoffed Jackal.

Tiger rushed at him, but Jackal dodged into a cleft in the rock. Tiger could not claw him out, for the opening was far too narrow. Jackal mocked and jeered, and Tiger tore the ground

in rage, but that did not help. So he ate all that he wanted and went home, while Jackal slipped off quietly.

But things could not remain like that. The days were long, and the world was a small place; one day they were going to come up against each other again.

So it happened that Jackal stood at the river, drinking, when suddenly he saw in the clear water Tiger's spotted body behind him. Flight was out of the question.

"Yes," Jackal said out loud to himself as if he knew nothing about Tiger, "they're getting on well." And he stared into the water.

Tiger was curious. "What's getting on well, Jackal?" he asked.

Jackal pretended to be surprised when he looked at Tiger. "Morning," he said. "I'm talking about the tiger skins that I have down there in the water to soften, so I can tan them."

"Tiger skins? How did you get hold of them?" asked Tiger.

"By catching tigers, of course," replied Jackal. "It's a good thing we're acquaintances, otherwise your skin would be lying there as well."

"Rot!" growled Tiger.

"Look for yourself," said Jackal.

Tiger looked and saw his own reflection in the mirror of the water. He was scared. "You're right," he said quickly. "Goodbye."

"Goodbye," said Jackal.

Tiger could not get over the fact that Jackal was such a dangerous tiger hunter. He bumped into Baboon and blurted it out, "Have you heard? Jackal's busy wiping out all tigers."

"Jackal?" said Baboon. "I don't believe it."

"Come with me and see for yourself."

"Fine, let's go," agreed Baboon.

"But I don't trust you!" said Tiger. "You have a big mouth now, but when we get near Jackal and he becomes dangerous, you'll jump into a tree. Then what happens to me?"

"We'll tie our tails together," suggested Baboon. "Then one cannot run away from the other."

"Good," said Tiger.

Jackal was sitting in front of his house, sharpening his assegai, when he saw them coming. "Now you need all your wits about you," he told himself. He called over his shoulder, "Wife, go inside. When I clear my throat, pinch the children till they scream."

"Very well, Husband," answered his wife, who also enjoyed a good joke.

Tiger and Baboon arrived, but Jackal kept at his assegai. He took notice of nothing else.

"Good day," said Tiger.

"Good day," said Baboon, "I hear . . ."

But before he could go any further, Jackal cleared his throat, and the children set up a howl. This was She-jackal's doing, but the two knew nothing about it.

"What's that?" asked Baboon.

"I wonder myself," answered Jackal. "Perhaps they want some more food." He shouted into the house, "Wife, why are the children crying? Are they hungry?"

"Yes, Husband," answered his wife. "They're absolutely ravenous."

Jackal sighed. "Dear me, will they never get enough? This very morning I brought them two tigers and three baboons. I'll have to do something about it." He looked at Tiger and Baboon, but they did not wait to say goodbye.

Tiger fled to the left, and Baboon to the right, but the knot in their tails held them back. Then they headed straight forward, but Baboon could not keep up. Before long he was being pulled bang! bang! bang! over the tufts of grass behind Tiger. Tiger thought it was Jackal on his heels, and he flew over the ground.

This is the reason why Baboon has such a shiny bottom, and it is from that day's happenings that the enmity between Tiger and Baboon arose, for each was shamed in front of the other. A tiger will attack a baboon whenever he can; and whenever the opportunity arises, a baboon will taunt a tiger.

Hare with the calabash of water

Time and again the land was stricken by drought, and the animals endured thirst. Finally King Lion said, "This cannot go on. Let us dig a dam below the spring. Then we'll always have something to drink." All the animals agreed that this was a good plan.

Only Hare was lazy. He lay to one side on a patch of couch grass and watched the others work.

"You must help, Hare," said the animals, "or you won't get any of the water."

"Who wants that old water?" declared Hare. "I drink with the king of the bees."

The animals worked hard. Within a few days the dam was finished. Then they stemmed the stream, and all stood and watched how the water gradually spread over the ground and slowly crept up the wall. "Now let the drought come," said King Lion, satisfied, and all the animals agreed, "Yes, now we'll always have something with which to quench our thirst."

Only Hare lay to one side on the couch grass and laughed. "Who wants that old water?" he said. "I drink with the king of the bees."

"We'll make sure that you get none of our water," growled King Lion. "Baboon, you are a sensible fellow. Tonight you must stand guard." The animals went into different directions to sleep or to eat, as was each one's habit. Hare dug up a few *uintjies*. Then he lay and sunned himself, but by the time evening came, he was thirsty. "A little spring water wouldn't taste too bad now," he said. "I must see what I can do."

He took two calabashes and went off to the dam. In one there was a little honey, but the other one was empty. As he walked, he sang:

Oh yes! Oh no!
And a heigh-ho!
Here comes Hare
Tiptoe.

From far off Baboon shouted at him, "You'd better stay away, Hare! This water's not for you."

"Who wants that old water?" asked Hare. "I drink with the king of bees."

He went and sat right in front of Baboon, dug some honey with a little stick from the calabash and licked it up with relish. Now Baboon had a sweet tooth. He tried to look away, but his eyes kept turning back to the honey. He tried to think of other things, but his mouth kept on watering.

"Give me some of that honey, Hare," he begged. "Then you can fill your calabash at the dam."

"Not likely," said Hare. "I know you. If I come close, you'll grab me. Then you'll go to the king and say I wanted to steal your water."

"No, never. Not I," said Baboon.

"Lie on your back, then I'll put a bit in your mouth," said Hare.

Baboon lay down. Hare pulled out a few of the rushes that grew beside the dam and bound his paws tightly together. Then he whisked off to the water, filled his calabash and walked away, singing:

Oh yes! Oh no!
And a heigh-ho!
Here goes Hare
Tiptoe.

The next morning the animals found Baboon lying there beside the water, and they knew immediately who had done it. But Baboon was too ashamed to talk. He just hung his head. Even today he cannot look anyone in the eyes.

"Cat," King Lion ordered, "you're a man who has seen the world. Tonight you'll stand guard." Then the animals went their separate ways again.

Hare spent the whole day feeding and lying in the sun. Every so often he took a drink from his calabash. By evening there was nothing left and he was still thirsty. "A drink of spring water wouldn't taste too bad," he thought. "I must see what I can do about it."

Again he took his two calabashes, the one with honey and the other one empty, and he walked to the dam, singing:

Oh yes! Oh no!
And a heigh-ho!
Here comes Hare
Tiptoe.

"You'd better stay away, Hare!" screamed Cat when he heard him. "You'll get no water here."

"Who wants that old water?" answered Hare. "I drink with the king of the bees."

He sat down by the dam and licked his honey stick until Cat could bear it no longer.

"Give me some of the honey, Hare," he begged. "Then you can fill your calabash at the dam."

"No, I'm not coming near you," said Hare. "You'll catch me and call the other animals to put me to death because I stole your water."

111

"No, never!" swore Cat.

"Wait," said Hare. "I'll put a bit of the bee king's water on this flat stone for you. Then you can lick it up." But in doing so, Hare also scraped out a bee that had landed in his calabash. Cat came up quickly. He licked with delight till he came to the bee. Whoops! it stung him on the nose.

"Ouch!" howled Cat, for the bee sting burnt like fire. He rubbed and scrubbed, but the burning did not die down. So he dived into the water to get away from the pain.

"Look out, Cat!" called Hare. "The bees are upon you."

Cat swam till the water rose in foamy waves. Dripping wet, he climbed out on the other side. In the meanwhile Hare had long finished filling his calabash and had gone away, singing:

Oh yes! Oh no!
And a heigh-ho!
Here goes Hare
Tiptoe.

The next morning King Lion was furious when he saw how bad Cat looked. He knew immediately that it was Hare's doing. Cat's nose was so swollen that he could scarcely talk, and even to this day he has to purr instead. And also Cat will not go near water, because he had quite enough of swimming that night.

"Who's going to stand guard tonight?" demanded King Lion, but all the animals were afraid of Hare. Only Tortoise struggled slowly up. "I shall," he said. The other animals laughed.

"How can you ever catch Hare?" asked King Lion. "You can scarcely drag your own body over the ground."

"Baboon is fast on his feet, and Cat is as agile as you can get," answered Tortoise, "yet neither of them could catch Hare. Now give me a chance."

"All right, then," King Lion said.

"Just spread a calabash full of birdlime over my back," said Tortoise. After they had done that, he walked slowly down to the dam and lay down right at the water line.

That evening Hare again loped down the little path to the dam with his two calabashes, singing:

Oh yes! Oh no!
And a heigh-ho!
Here comes Hare
Tiptoe.

He came to the dam, but saw no one. "Baboon!" he called. "Cat!" No, all was quiet. "They're frightened," he thought to himself. "They know that they can't keep me away." Then he walked right up to the edge of the water. There he saw

Tortoise's back shining in the moonlight. "There's even a stepping stone, perfect to ladle from," he said out loud as he climbed on Tortoise's back and filled his calabash.

But when it came to climbing off, the trouble started. His hind legs were stuck.

"Now, what sort of a stone is this?" asked Hare, and he tugged and tugged to break free.

"Hee, hee, hee!" laughed Tortoise.

"Oh, indeed!" said Hare. "You think you can snigger at me. I'll bash you to pieces!" Ker-swip! There his left front foot was gripped fast. Ker-swap! And his right front foot too!

"Ha, ha, ha," laughed Tortoise.

"An impudent stone, this one," fumed Hare. "I'll give him such a dusting-off with my ears that the splinters will fly."

Kar-biff! That was his right ear that got stuck.

Kar-baff! That was his left.

"Ho, ho, ho!" laughed Tortoise.

"Let me go! Let me go!" screamed Hare. He tugged and lugged in a frenzy.

Tortoise rose slowly. "I've got you now, Hare," he said and started walking.

"It's you, is it?" said Hare. "I'll tear your shell into a thousand pieces." He wrenched so hard with his feet and ears that Tortoise's back was pulled up into knobbly patches, which is why Tortoise looks so rough and scabby today. But the birdlime held firm, and Hare could not break free.

Tortoise walked until he got to King Lion's house. The sun was already up before he arrived.

"Well done, Tortoise!" roared Lion, and all the animals ran up to have a look.

"See how the water thief's ears hang now," they laughed. It was true. Hare really looked miserable. His whole body was covered with birdlime, and he was dead beat from struggling.

"Oh, mighty King," said Hare, acting humble, "I acknowledge that I have done wrong and that I deserve death. Grant me only that I die as becomes a hare."

"And how would you like to die?" asked King Lion.

"Let someone grip my tail and dash my head against a rock."

"That doesn't sound like a bad plan," said King Lion.

"I'll do it, my King," Baboon said immediately. He had not forgotten how Hare had fooled him.

"Right you are, Baboon. We're waiting," said King Lion.

Baboon came up, gripped Hare by the tail, tore him off Tortoise's back and swung him, one, two, three times in the air above his head. But, just as he gathered himself for the death-blow, there was a rip, and Baboon stood with a little stump in his hand, while Hare sailed out into the blue. His tail had broken off clean!

"Goodbye, your Highness," Hare called over his shoulder. "Please excuse me if I'm in a hurry, but my children must be very thirsty." And he slid away through the grass, grabbed his calabash of water and made tracks to his house.

"Good gracious, Hare," his wife said when he got home. "Why do you look so ghastly from behind?"

"I was playing with the children, Wife," says Hare, "and I got a bit chafed."

From that day onwards Hare drank no more water, he only licked the dew from the grass.

Lion's wife

One day King Lion got furious with his wife. She tried to duck out of his way, but he grabbed her by the mane, for in those days female lions still had swanky collars. Then he dragged her through the bushes. He dragged her till her neck was rubbed smooth and her mane hung in tiny bits and pieces on the thorns.

"Just look at that," said the other female lions when they saw this. "Fine manes bring misfortune only. One of these days our husbands will also maul us around like that when they get annoyed with us." So they went to find Muskrat to gnaw their manes off.

This is the reason why nowadays lionesses have bare necks.

Sheikh Yussuf
A Cape Malay tale

In the olden days when the Netherlands was a great trading country and its laden sailing ships voyaged around the Cape of Good Hope, Sheikh Yussuf was a powerful leader of his people in the rich spice lands of the Far East. He was taken prisoner in a war against the Dutch and finally banished to the Cape, for the Dutch were afraid that his people would rebel again if he remained there. He lived and worked in the Cape, propagating the Islam faith until his death a few years later – a remarkable man, a great prince and religious leader. But after his death his kramat or grave remained neglected and forgotten.

119

Many years later, so it is told, there lived a little shepherd called Agmat. One day Agmat happened to herd his sheep into the dunes. The sun was warm, his sheep were grazing peacefully, and Agmat fell asleep. He woke with a start to find that the sun was setting behind the sea, and his sheep were nowhere to be seen. Agmat searched and searched: up a dune here, down a gully there. No sheep were to be found.

Now Agmat was in trouble. He could not go back to the farm, for there he would get a whale of a thrashing. He did not want to stay where he was, for the darkness held many terrors. Agmat searched until he was lost himself, and then he could do no more. He dug himself a resting place against a sandbank and curled himself into a ball.

The young boy listened to the night animals and shivered. He thought of what the morning would bring and shook with fear. But a great drowsiness overcame him and he fell asleep, and while he slept he dreamed. In his dream there stood before him a man in a long, green robe. Agmat bowed down to the ground, for he knew at once that this was a holy man. But when he looked up, the man in the green robe had gone.

Agmat slept again, but the man of his dreams came back.

"Agmat," he said.

Agmat bowed low.

"Agmat," he said again.

Agmat bowed and bowed.

"Agmat," he said for the third time.

Only then did Agmat find his tongue. "I hear you, Lord," he said.

"Do you know me?" asked the man.

"No, I know you not, Lord," said Agmat

"We voyaged on a ship from a far land," the man told him. "The people became very thirsty, but there was no water. I put my foot in the sea, and the salt water became sweet so that they could drink."

"Now I know!" called out Agmat. "You are Sheikh Yussuf."

He fell into a deeper sleep, and the man vanished. But then he came a third time.

"Agmat," he said, "you know me now, and I know you. I know your trouble, but you need not fear. Your sheep are safe. Tomorrow morning go eastwards to the third dune from here, and you will find them. But there will be more to be found than the sheep, and you must tell your people about it." The man with the long, green robe passed out of Agmat's dream, and he did not appear again.

The next morning, when the sun woke him, Agmat sat up. He thought of his sheep and he thought of his dreams. "The third dune from here to the east," he said, for he remembered everything exactly as the man had told him. Quickly he set out.

Yes, there at the third dune his sheep were grazing as if they had never been lost. Agmat began to gather them together at once until he thought, recalling his dream, "But there will be more to be found there than the sheep . . ." He looked round, here in a gully and there on a dune. Then he saw, on a hillock between the grass and the bushes – an old, old grave. He knew that this was the thing of which the man had spoken.

Agmat took the sheep home and the farmer was so glad that he did not even scold him. Then he went to tell his people and they could hardly believe their ears.

"It must be the holy man's grave," they said. "We shall take care that it is not forgotten again."

The built a beautiful cupola, hung with the finest embroidery. And today still the Malays come from far and near to pray at Sheikh Yussuf's grave.

The incompetent judge

Canary and Crow fell out one day over which of them was the
better singer. "This is no good," Canary said finally, exhausted
with arguing. "We must find a judge."

"Fine," agreed Crow. "We'll ask the first animal we come
across."

Off they flew until they saw Pig lying in a puddle of mud.
Canary put their case. "M-m-m!" said Pig. "Sing!"

Canary tilted his head back. He sang of the sun and the
golden day till all the other birds fell quiet, and the wind kept
still to listen, and even the old weeping willow tree lifted its
branches a little.

But Crow went to sit beside Pig. He scratched Pig's back with his long, sharp claws so that Pig grunted, "Ee, eeh, eeh!" with pleasure. Then Crow cawed, "Ka, ka, kah!" in Pig's ear.

"Crow sings better," said Pig, without thinking twice about the matter.

Canary shook his head sadly. "This is what happens when a canary allows a pig to judge him," he said. And he spread his wings and flew away.

Baboon and the ouchy pears

Baboon loved to tease Hare. Whenever Hare went to feed in Farmer's lettuce field, Baboon went to sit high in the fig tree and screamed, "Farmer, come quickly! Hare is in the garden."

Then Farmer came with his dogs and his gun. He was so angry with Hare over a few old lettuce leaves, that he completely forgot about Baboon and the figs.

It went on like this for a week. Hare had already complained several times to Baboon. Each time Baboon answered with soft words and promised better behaviour, but he was not a man of his word. "Very well, then," said Hare to himself. "He who will not listen, must be punished." He kept his eyes open. Then he loped off to Baboon.

"Yes, what is it, little Hare?" asked Baboon and he sniggered behind his hand. "More complaints?"

"No complaints this time, Uncle Baboon," answered Hare.

"Poor little Hare," said Baboon, swallowing a chuckle, "you had to run for your life this morning. Farmer's greyhound is very quick on his feet."

"I enjoy a bit of a run early in the day," answered Hare. "It's good for the health."

"That's right, Hare," said Baboon, openly guffawing. "You always moaned so much about my calling Farmer and his dogs, but I was really only doing it for your own good."

"Of course, I understand, Uncle Baboon," said Hare. "And that's why I want to do something for you in return. I see that Farmer has some beautiful pears, but I can't get at them. Could you not pick them? There are more than enough for us both."

"We could do that, Hare," said Baboon, and his mouth started watering. "Thank you. But aren't the pears early this year?"

"This is a new type," answered Hare. "They say even your eyes water when you taste them."

Quite amicably they set off down the little path to Farmer's orchard. It was already dusk, but Baboon did not want to wait.

Hare led the way for Baboon until they were among the trees where the first little pears were only just beginning to swell. He showed him some wasps' nests that hung high in the branches. "There they are, uncle Baboon," said Hare, "those fat, red ones. But pick them quickly, for it seems to me that I see something moving at Farmer's house."

Baboon did not disappoint him. It was just a step here and a step there, a skip and a hop, a good hold – and then he went straight for the choicest prize.

But he should not have done that at all. Wasp was just lying down, when he felt his whole house shudder and shake. Before he could get up, something broke the roof wide open. Now Wasp did not know what fear was, so he never thought of flight. "Attack!" he screamed, and he led the charge with his sting.

Baboon sat up straight. These were peculiar pears for sure. They tasted just like earth, and when you bit them, they bit you back. Baboon spat out what he could not swallow, and he let go what he held. But by then Baboon was being attacked by Wasp and his whole family – his uncles and aunts and nephews and nieces, and his in-laws too. Baboon ducked and

swiped and fell right down through the branches till he hit the
ground with a bang, but the wasps kept on stinging.

"How's it going, Uncle Baboon?" asked Hare. "Are your eyes
watering already?"

"Ou-ou-ouch!" moaned Baboon, and he shot off.

"Why're you so mingy, uncle Baboon?" Hare called after
him. "Don't I get any?"

"Ou-ou-ouch!" howled Baboon.

"Well, well," said Hare, "perhaps I'd better not taste such
ouchy pears." And he loped off to the lettuce beds.

Til Owlglass
I. The truth is painful

Til Owlglass's father died when Til was still a young boy. Father Owlglass had never liked work very much while he was alive, so his family was left completely unprovided for.

Til came upon his mother, weeping sadly. "Now, Mother," he asked, "what's the matter?"

"Your father is dead," she sobbed. "Who can take his place?"

"I can, Mother," answered Til.

"You?" said his mother. "You're just a silly little ass!"

"Only give me a bowl of porridge, Mother, then I'll show you," answered Til.

"And what do you mean by that?" she asked.

"Well, you always said Father took

more porridge out of the door in his stomach than he brought bread in for his family."

"You ill-mannered child!" shouted his mother, and she boxed his ears. "Have you no respect for the dead?"

Crying, Til went to sit in the street. Just then a woman with a squint came by. "What's wrong, my child?" she asked. "My mother hit me because I spoke the truth," snivelled Til.

"Shame!" said the woman. "That was not a nice thing to do. There are so many people who tell lies that you should not punish the truth. Here, go and buy some sweets." And she thrust a penny into his hand.

"Thank you, squinter," said Til.

"What!" shouted the woman, and she slapped his ear. "Have you no respect for your elders?" Furious, she walked off.

"Oho!" sighed Til:

Telling the truth makes one very sore,
Of that there is no doubt.
Truth is the thing everyone longs for,
Till some fool hands it out.

2. The clever crow

All that Owlglass and his brother inherited after their father's death, were two lean old horses. Brother Hans went into service, horse and all, and struggled hard to earn some money, but Brother Til did not like to work at all. He rode from farm to farm, trying to keep body and soul together without too much effort, till one day his horse got the bots and died. Til skinned him and walked off with the skin over his shoulder.

He had not gone far before he saw a small black crow sitting under a tree. The little bird had hurt its wing and could not fly.

"Bad company's better than none," said Owlglass, and he put the crow in his pocket.

The horse skin he sold at the first village he came to, but before he did so, he cut off a piece. He bought himself a basket, put the crow inside, covered it up with the skin and walked on.

He took service with a rich farmer, but the man was a real miser. Outside, on the farm, they worked like slaves, but inside, at the table, there was only dry bread and black coffee.

The farmer ate greedily, and Owlglass also had to tuck in, or he would die of hunger.

But the mistress of the house said, "No, thank you, Husband. I want nothing. My head aches too badly."

The second day it was her stomach that was sore, and the third day she just did not feel at all well.

"There's something fishy about this," said Owlglass to himself. Just after the meal he slipped quietly away from work. He peered through the window, and there was the farmer's wife dining on a delicious meal of meat, rice and stewed fruit.

The next day, who should be sick, but Owlglass himself – so sick that he could not leave his room. But when the farmer had gone to the fields, he got up quietly and watched the woman from the door that was slightly ajar. He saw her frying sausages and boiling potatoes and even making stew dumplings. Then she put everything carefully away before she took out the dry bread and coffee for the midday meal.

When the farmer sat down at the table, Owlglass also arrived, bringing his crow in the basket along.

"That's how it goes, eh?" grumbled the farmer. "Too sick to work, but well enough to eat."

"Yes," said Owlglass, "that's how it goes, Sir. Your wife again, is healthy enough to work, but too sick to eat."

Just as the farmer started his meal, Owlglass kicked the basket. "Caw, ca, ca!" croaked the crow. "Hush!" said Owlglass. "You must not speak of that."

"What must he not speak of?" asked the farmer.

"It's a big secret, Sir," said Owlglass. "If I told you about it, you'd be very cross."

"No, I will not," promised the farmer. "Tell me."

"The crow says there's a pan of sausages in the oven," said Owlglass.

The woman went pale, but the farmer growled, "The crow's talking nonsense," and took a bite of bread.

"You can't say that till you've seen with your own eyes," Owlglass persisted.

"Well, go and look then," said the farmer. In two ticks, Owlglass was back with the sausages.

"What on earth . . .?" began the farmer, but Owlglass lifted his finger. "You promised not to be angry," he said.

"That's true," agreed the farmer, and he cut himself a big piece of sausage. "Help yourself."

"Thank you," said Owlglass, and he served himself with the rest of the sausage, for the woman was too sick to eat.

Before the farmer could take his first bite, Owlglass kicked again and the crow croaked, "Caw, caw!"

"What now?" asked the farmer.

"You will not be cross, Sir?" asked Owlglass.

"No," promised the farmer.

"He says there are boiled potatoes in the linen press."

This time the farmer went to fetch them himself.

When the sausages and the potatoes were finished, Owlglass made sure that the crow spoke for the third time. So he told the man of the stew dumplings in the outer room.

"Thank you," said the farmer when they had finished. "I've not eaten so well for a long time."

"You could eat like this every day, Sir," said Owlglass, "if you would only allow your wife to cook. She's good at it. And her health would doubtlessly also improve."

"That's very true, Husband," said his wife eagerly. "No one can live on dry bread and black coffee all the time."

"Very well," said the farmer, "from tomorrow onwards you may cook for us." Then he turned again to Owlglass. "But tell me, how did your little crow know about all this?"

"Oh, this is not just an ordinary little crow," answered

Owlglass. "He can foretell the future, and anything you want to know."

"Really?" said the farmer, and his eyes shone greedily. He was already adding up the money such a clever bird could earn for him. "Won't you sell him to me? I'll give you a golden pound."

"Never," said Owlglass, "that's no price for a bird like this."

"Two golden pounds," said the farmer.

"No," said Owlglass, but the farmer persisted till Owlglass finally handed the little crow over to him for a whole bag full of golden pounds. Then, in high spirits, he set off for home.

"And where did you get all that money?" asked his brother Hans when he saw the gold.

"Don't you know that horse skins fetch such high prices at the market nowadays?" said Owlglass.

Hans immediately went and shot the horse that had helped him to earn his little bit of bread each day. Then he went off to the market with the skin. But people laughed at him when he talked of golden pounds and in the end he had to be content to take a few pieces of silver for it.

3. Broken china

After he had sent his brother on a wild-goose chase that cost him his horse, Owlglass had to make himself scarce at home. He rambled round the farm out of harm's way, and it was not long before he came to the garbage dump. Among the other rubbish there lay ever so many broken pieces of china accumulated over the years. The bits sparkled in the sun – one with a rose pattern, another with forget-me-nots, some with coloured squares and stripes. Owlglass thought they were very pretty. He started collecting them, and soon he had a sack full.

Then he hauled the sack onto his shoulder and took to the road.

That evening he stayed at an inn, but before he went to his room, he called the landlord aside and whispered in his ear, "I have with me a whole sack full of money. Where can I hide it so that it will be safe?"

"We're honest people here," the landlord said, offended. "Just leave it there in the front room. No one will touch it."

"Fine, if you say so," answered Owlglass, and he put it down.

In the middle of the night, when the household slept, Owl-glass came quietly and fetched the sack, stole out of the front door, emptied it beside a stream, and filled it with little stones. Then he stowed it in the front room again and went to sleep like the rest.

The next morning, before he departed, he opened the sack. Then he shouted loudly, "Thief! Thief! Help, I've been robbed!"

The landlord came running. "Not so loud, fellow," he said. "You'll drag my inn's name through the mud. What's happened?"

"I put my sack of money down here," said Owlglass. "You saw me do it yourself. Now it's filled with stones from the river."

The landlord was full of sweet words, but Owlglass threat-ened him with the police and the court. Finally he was obliged to fill the sack with money to save the name of his inn.

"What's this?" asked Owlglass's brother Hans when he arrived with the sack of money. Hans knew that Owlglass had left with a load of broken china.

"People are going crazy over bits of china," said Owlglass. "I sold all mine immediately at the crockery shop at the corner."

"I'm going too," shouted Hans. He grabbed a stick and began to lay left and right into his mother's cups, saucers and plates. She tried to stop him, but he did not cease till everything was in bits and pieces. Yet this time he did not even get a little silver as he had done for his horse's skin. People laughed him to scorn for being so silly as to try to sell broken china.

4. The death penalty for a ne'er-do-well

Til's brother Hans went to complain to the judge about Owlglass's tricks. "What a good-for-nothing," said the judge when he had heard it all. "He deserves the death penalty. Constable!" he called. "Go and drown this man in the river."

The constable stuffed Owlglass into a sack, bound it tight and got a friend to help him carry it. Then they set off towards the river.

After a while, Owlglass asked from inside the sack, "Did you bring a long stick with you?"

"No," said the constable.

"Why?" asked his friend.

"To push me under the water, of course," said Owlglass. "I won't sink by myself, you know."

"Yes, that's true," said the constable to his friend. "We'd better go find a stick first."

So they put Owlglass down beside the road and went off.

Then Owlglass started to shout. "I won't! I won't! I won't be king!" He kept on in this fashion until a shepherd with his sheep came by. "I want to be king," the shepherd said when he heard Owlglass lamenting.

"Then let me out and climb into this sack here," said Owlglass.

"With pleasure," said the shepherd.

Owlglass fastened the shepherd up securely, gathered his sheep and drove them off. When the constables came back, Owlglass was far away. The shepherd had a great deal of polite explaining to do, or he would have landed in the river.

"What's this?" said Hans, his brother, when Owlglass arrived home with the sheep. "I thought they'd gone to drown you."

"They threw me into the river, yes, that's true," Owlglass told him, "but then I came upon the biggest herd of sheep I've ever seen in my life. It was a pity that I was alone, otherwise I should've been able to drive away many more."

Hans did not let the grass grow under his feet. He made tracks to the river. As he ran, he called whomever he saw on the way to come with him to help with the watersheep. They hesitated on the bank at first, but when they saw the white tops of the stones on the riverbed, nothing could stop them. "The sheep! Look at all the sheep!" they called to one another and dived in.

Owlglass just shook his head and said:

The biggest sheep was born without
Wool upon his back.
But between his ears he carries
About a well-stuffed sack.

Then he went off, whistling. And the poor, silly sheep seekers had to find their own way out of the river.

139

5. A hard night's rest

Owlglass made sure that he cleared right out of the district, for he knew that if his brother Hans got his hands on him, there would surely be a murder. So it came about that late that evening he was asking for a place to sleep at a farm. The farmer's wife was sorry for him because he looked dead beat and she gave him a big feather bed to sleep in.

Owlglass had never in all his life slept on a feather bed and he stood for a long time looking at the mattress. Then he pulled out one small feather and lay down upon that.

The next morning he came from the outside room, very stiff indeed.

"How did you sleep?" asked the woman.

"Hard, thank you," answered Owlglass.

"How can that be?" asked the woman, astonished. "I gave you such a soft feather bed."

"It was a good thing that I didn't even try to lie on it," answered Owlglass. "I slept on one feather – that was bad enough. How hard do you think a whole mattress of feathers would've been?"

6. Hewer of wood, carrier of water

Owlglass took service on a farm, and for the first few days things didn't go too badly.

Saturday afternoon the farmer wanted to go visiting friends. Before he drove off, he said to Owlglass, "Make sure that there's enough water and wood in the house. Tomorrow is Sunday, and we don't want to be bothered with such things then."

"I'll see to it," promised Til. As soon as the farmer had left, he began to bring in wood. He packed the front room full, and the bedrooms and the passage. Then he began with the water. The big tub in the kitchen soon overflowed, but Owlglass just went on pouring. The water streamed over the floor and the back verandah, and it seeped in at the dining-room door.

Late that evening the farmer and his wife came back. The man nearly tripped over the wood in the passage. Furious, he went round to the back door,

but he was walking too hastily and his feet slipped from under him on the wet verandah.

"Where's that man?" he shouted, mad with rage.

"Here I am," answered Owlglass, coming up with another bucket of water.

"And what do you think you're doing?" asked the farmer.

"I'm only trying to do my work," answered Owlglass. "I've brought in enough wood. Now I just have to get enough water into the house before the clock strikes twelve, for then it's Sunday."

"I'll kill you if I get my hands on you!" yelled the farmer, and he rushed at Owlglass.

"You won't get a chance!" answered Owlglass, and he was off.

7. The golden bird

Owlglass put as many miles as possible between the angry farmer and himself, but the man stayed on his track. One afternoon Owlglass fell asleep, exhausted, behind a small patch of thorn bushes. While he was rubbing the sleep out of his eyes, the farmer nearly tripped over him. Owlglass took one look and was ready with another plan.

He picked up his hat from the ground, threw it over a pile of fresh manure that a grazing cow had left and began to sing softly:

> Golden bird! Golden bird!
> Before you fly away,
> Lay an egg, lay an egg,
> Lay an egg, I pray!

"Aha!" shouted the farmer when he saw Owlglass, and he would have thrashed him then and there.

"Hush!" said Owlglass. "Don't make such a noise. The golden bird will be frightened; then he won't lay an egg."

"What golden bird?" asked the farmer curiously.

"Here under my hat," replied Owlglass. "He lays golden eggs. I wish I had a small cage, then I could catch him."

"Cage? And where are you going to find a cage?" asked the farmer.

"That's no problem," said Owlglass.

The farmer's eyes glistened with avarice. "Go and get it then, and hurry up," he commanded. "I'll watch the bird in the meantime."

"Thanks," said Owlglass, and he did not wait to be told twice.

While Owlglass vanished round the thorn bushes, the farmer squatted beside the hat and sang the song as he had heard Owlglass sing it:

Golden bird! Golden bird!
Before you fly away,
Lay an egg, lay an egg,
Lay an egg, I pray!

He gave the bird ample time.
When he reckoned that he
must surely be finished,
he cupped his hands and
pushed them slowly
under the hat to catch him
in one fell swoop. He had
of course not the slightest
intention of waiting for
Owlglass and his cage.

He grabbed, but there was no bird.
He felt only a wetness between
his fingers. Just then a
cow lowed on the rise, and
the farmer knew that
Owlglass had outwitted
him once again.

8. Old age

At an inn where Owlglass stayed one night, he happened to get the room next to the landlord's. The walls were thin, and his ears were sharp. He heard the landlord counting his gold until late.

"Why do you keep all that money?" the man's wife asked at last. "Rather give it to me to buy new clothes."

"No, we must put something away for old age," answered the landlord.

The next day, when the man had gone to town, Owlglass went to the woman and said. "I am Old Age. I've just come to get my money."

"Oh, is it for you that he has been scrimping," the woman said. "He's been heaping up money for years." And she brought all her husband's money and gave it to Owlglass.

"This won't last till my old age, surely," said Til to himself as he walked off. "But it will come in very handy today – and tomorrow, and the next day too!"

The cleft in the mountain

Cousin Mat and cousin Japhet went hunting. They found little in the open, so they tried the mountain, but game was still scarce. Rather tired and dejected, they unsaddled under a big tree.

"I'll get a fire going in the meantime," said Mat. "Then we can boil some water."

"I'll go and get some water," said Japhet. "Then we can make some coffee." He followed the sound of a little stream, but the spring was deeper in the ravine than he had thought and when he tried to climb down to it, his feet slipped and he fell into a cleft.

"Help! Help!" he shouted.

"Help! Help!" shouted the echo.

Mat, sitting by his fire, jumped up with a start. "I'm coming, Japhet!" he called.

So Mat searched, while his cousin groaned, and the echo mocked him. Finally Mat found him, but the cleft was too deep for him to get to Japhet and too narrow to climb in.

"I'll just find a long branch," said Mat.

"Hurry! Please hurry!" begged Japhet.

"Hurry!" begged the echo too.

But the longest branch that Mat could find was still too short to reach his cousin.

"I'll go and fetch a strap," said Mat.

"Hurry! Only hurry!" pleaded Japhet.

"Hurry!" pleaded the echo.

Mat brought the strap, but he could not get a loop around his cousin, for the cleft was far too narrow. And Japhet could not take hold of it, for his two arms were stuck.

The day grew hotter, and Japhet was weakening.

"I'm done for," he groaned.

148

"I'm done for," groaned the echo.

Mat was at his wits' end and he did not know what to say, but Japhet spoke again, "Go and get my gun. Then you can put me out of my misery."

"Never!" shouted Mat. "How can I shoot my own cousin?"

"How can you see your cousin die here of hunger and thirst?" asked Japhet.

They talked and argued in this manner, until Mat saw for himself that there was no other way out. With a heavy heart, he walked away. Clumsily his fingers loaded the gun. With tears in his eyes he came back to the cleft.

"Farewell, cousin," he whispered.

"Farewell," whispered Japhet.

"Farewell," whispered the echo.

Mat's finger curled over the trigger. Suddenly there was a thundering and a shaking. The gun fell out of his hands. It clattered onto the stones, and the echo clattered along.

Mat shut his eyes tight, rather than to see what was happening. He put his fingers in his ears, rather than to hear what was going on. He was too scared to speak.

Finally he opened his eyes. He let his hands fall. "What was that?" he asked aloud.

"Why don't you help me?" asked a voice. It was Japhet.

"Don't you help me?" asked the echo.

Then Mat finally understood that there had been an earthquake that had torn the mountain wider open so that Japhet now lay free in a ravine. Quickly he climbed down and helped him out. After Mat had given him a cup of coffee, Japhet felt much better.

"Whew!" sighed Mat. "That was almost the end of you."

"Almost," agreed Japhet.

"Almost," agreed the echo.

The Enchanted Forest
A Khoikhoi tale

Once upon a time a man and his wife followed the game far away on the other side of the Great River. They had only one child – a small boy. The father was a fine shot and, armed as he was with his old musket and his powder horn, he had need of nothing else to fill the pot. So the family was content.

But one day they put their little son down to sleep under a broom bush while they went to fetch water at the river. There they were killed by a band of plundering robbers. When the little boy woke with a start, he was alone in the world. He began

to cry, but that did not help. He screamed louder, but no mother came to comfort him. He had struggled to his feet and stood woebegone, whimpering, when an old witchdoctor happened to come by. The old man picked up the child. Taking the gun and the powder horn, he followed the tracks to the river where he saw what had happened. Then he took the child back to his hut.

"A terrible thing happened, Wife," he said and told the story.

"I don't want a child," mumbled his wife sullenly.

"My magic bones say he's very good-natured," answered the witchdoctor. "He'll be no trouble."

"I don't want anything to do with a child," grumbled his wife sourly, but the witchdoctor kept on until, in the end, she finally said yes.

The child grew up, and he was well behaved and obedient, just as the old witchdoctor's bones had said. The old man loved him as if he were his own son, but his stepmother could not bear the sight of him. If anything went wrong, it was always his fault. He got more beatings than food. From morning to night she scolded the boy, whom she called Good-for-Nothing.

One day, when he had grown into a fine lad, Good-for-Nothing came to the old witchdoctor. "Father," he said, "you have always been very good to me, but I can't bear any more."

The old man was sick at heart, but he said, "I understand, my son. What will you do?"

"I'm going away," replied the boy. "Somewhere surely I'll find a place where I can be happy."

The old man loosened the thongs of his leather pouch of bones and, after he had talked to them for a long while, he threw them on the ground. He sat even longer looking at them. "It will go well with you, my son," he said finally. "Only beware of the Enchanted Forest."

"I'll be careful," said Good-for-Nothing.

Then the witchdoctor gave him his own father's gun, which

he had kept all the time, and his father's powder horn, and a knobbed stick as a kerrie. "Don't lose this, he said, "for it is a magic weapon. While you have it, no one can stand against you."

"Thank you, Father. I'll keep it safe," said Good-for-Nothing. Then he bade the old man goodbye and walked off.

Good-for-Nothing walked the whole day. At midday he shot two guineafowl with his father's old gun. He threw them over his shoulder and walked on. That evening he came to a forest.

"I must beware," he said to himself. "Perhaps this is the Enchanted Forest."

Suddenly, before he could turn away, a bird high in the trees began to sing:

Cheep, cheep, chee! Cheep, cheep, chee!
Come with me! Come with me!
Cheep, cheep, chee! Cheep, cheep, chee!
Where I fly free; where I fly free . . .
Cheep, cheep, chee! Cheep, cheep, chee!
All is green, all is gold –
Cheep, cheep, chee! Cheep, cheep, chee!
In the forest's heart, so old.

The bird sang so beautifully that Good-for-Nothing completely forgot the old witchdoctor's words. He forgot to be careful, and he forgot about the Enchanted Forest. All he knew, was that he did not want to loose the bird again, and that he wanted to be with him forever. So he followed the bird that flew ever further and further on in front of him. It was, indeed, a wood spirit who had disguised himself as a bird and sang so sweetly to lead people astray.

Good-for-Nothing walked and walked. He was not afraid, for was not the bird there? He walked and walked until night fell in the forest, but he did not turn back, for he wanted to be with the bird. Then, suddenly, the bird was gone, and there was no song among the branches. Good-for-Nothing stood still and looked round, but he could see nothing. He tried to remember the way he had come, but he had not kept track. Then Good-for-Nothing knew that he was lost, and that this must be the Enchanted Forest.

"I must not be afraid," he said bravely, "because I have my father's powder horn."

He gathered some wood and lit a fire. When the flames burnt high, he saw several skeletons lying around. He knew

154

that they were those of people who had been lost in the forest.

"I'm not frightened," said Good-for-Nothing boldly, "because I have my father's gun."

He went up to the skeletons. Near one of them lay a bottle of wine. He took it and drank, for he was very thirsty. Then he roasted his guineafowl over the fire. After he had eaten, he lay down and went to sleep.

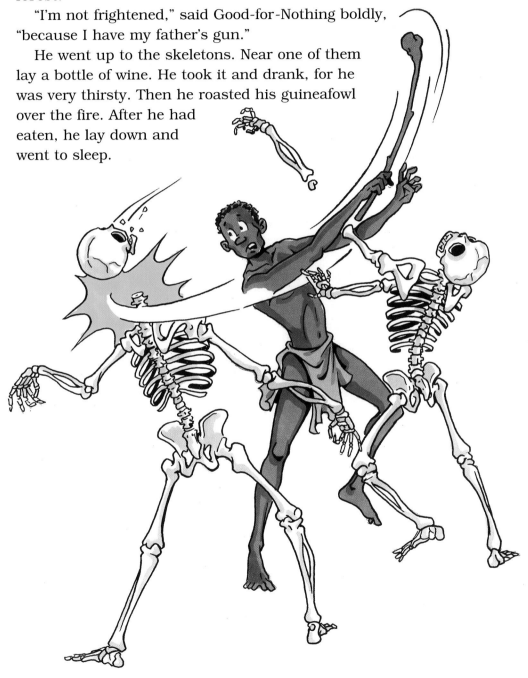

Suddenly, in the middle of the night, he was awakened by the strangest noise: clipper, clap! clipper, clap! What on earth could it be? He looked towards the fire and there he saw all the skeletons sitting by the red coals, smoking pipe. It was their bones that clipper-clapped when they moved.

Good-for-Nothing was frightened out of his wits, but he took another gulp of wine and plucked up courage. At the top of his voice he called out to the smokers, "I say, good evening, my friends."

He should not have done that. Knerst! their heards turned as one man towards him. Claa, claa, claa! their bones clapped together as they ran at him. A powder horn and a gun were not going to help him in this plight, thought Good-for-Nothing. He would have to use his magic stick.

He charged at the skeletons and hit out right and left among them so that the splinters flew.

"So there!" he said when all was quiet again.

"I wasn't doing anything to you. Why did you attack me?"

Something moved on the other side
of the fire and Good-for-Nothing glimpsed
the whiteness of two more skeletons. He lifted
his magic stick.

"Don't hit us," said a hollow voice. "We are your
murdered father and mother. We followed you when
the wood spirit led you astray. Wait till morning,
then we'll show you the path."

"Thank you, Father," said Good-for-Nothing.
"Thank you, Mother." And he went back
to sleep.

Early next morning his parents took
him out of the Enchanted Forest,
as they had promised.

Good-for-Nothing lived long
and happily and travelled
many far paths. But he
never saw his parents again,
and he made sure that
he was never again
tricked by a
wood spirit.

The stupid farmer

One day an old farmer with a long, flowing beard rode into town. There he came upon three students who immediately decided that they would make fun of this silly old man.

"Good morning, Father Abraham," said the first student.

"Good morning, Father Isaac," said the second student.

"Good morning, Father Jacob," said the third student.

"No," said the old farmer, "I'm not Abraham, Isaac or Jacob. I am Saul, the sun of Kish, who went to look for his father's donkeys, and it seems to me as though I've found them."

The students felt rather foolish, and behind the old man's back they said to one another, "Let's invite him for lunch. Then we'll show him."

At the hotel they ordered three fine herrings and one miser-

able bloater. They each took a herring, while the old man got the bloater. The students winked at one another, for they thought they had played a fine trick on him. But before they started to eat, they noticed that the old man was talking to the bloater.

"What are you saying to that fish, old fellow?" the first student asked curiously.

"Well," said the farmer, "my father drowned years ago in the sea. I wondered if I could hear anything about that from him. He says he's too young; I must ask the big fish."

"Here's my herring," said the student. "Ask him."

Again the old man spoke quietly.

"What does he say?" inquired the student.

"He says I must ask his brother."

The second student pushed his fish nearer.

"He says his sister is sure to know," the old man declared solemnly, after he had quietly interrogated that fish. "She's a real old gossip."

So he got the third fish as well.

"She says that the sea creatures ate my father up," said the old man, after listening for a long time. "And now I may eat them." The students had to sit and watch how the herrings disappeared, one by one, down the farmer's throat – and the bloater too.

"Let's ask him to dinner as well," the students said among themselves. "Then we'll definitely teach him a lesson."

That evening they ordered a big fish and cut it into three pieces.

"Where three or four are gathered together," said the first student, "one must have the head." And he took it.

"Where three or four are gathered together," said the second student, "someone must have the body." And he took it.

"Where three or four are gathered together, someone must have the tail," said the third student. And he took the last piece.

There was nothing left for the old man. He stood up slowly, while the students smiled to one another at how they had out-smarted him. "Where three are gathered together who do not have any manners," said the old man, "the fourth must teach them." And he took up his sjambok and gave them a proper thrashing.

The disappearance of the piebald bee

My father was the best bee farmer of all (a youngster once told me). Yes, surely, there had never been a bee farmer like him. The whole farm was covered with hives. We lost count of them. What we did then was to count the bees and divide the number by ten thousand and one. Because, as Father always said, there are ten thousand bees in a swarm – plus, of course, the queen bee. And just to be sure that none of them got lost, we branded them F.B. on their left hindquarters. Obviously, this stood for "Father's Bee".

So, well and good, nothing could be better. Then one morning I found that one particular bee, a piebald with a white front leg, was missing.

"Go and look for him," said my father.

"You could say I've already started looking, Father," I answered.

I went to the chicken paddock, saddled my black cock and rode off. Just to refresh him a little if he perhaps got hungry, I took half a bag of maize and a sack of chaff along.

The track was not difficult to follow, for the bee was shod. So I rode for two days. On the third day I came to a colossal hippo pool, one hundred and fifty miles across. Luckily there was an island about twenty-five miles from the bank. I poked my cock under the short ribs with my heels, and he sprang away at such a pace that the maize slipped off the saddle and landed in the water. But nothing could stop the black cock. He rowed so powerfully with his wings that they strained like a wagon's canvas in the wind and whenever they hit the water, it sounded like cannon shots. I had to look back every now and again to make sure that it was really not someone shooting at me.

Having arrived at the island, I found a man ploughing, with the piebald bee harnassed in front. I could not rebuke him too sternly, for if he had not put the bee to work, he might possibly have gone further.

So all I said was, "Thank you very much," and the man said, "The pleasure's mine. It's a long time since I've had such a hard-working draught bee."

Then I hobbled the cock so that he could have a bit of a rest, gave him a little fodder to peck at and went to lie down for a while. When we had had a rest, I saddled up the bee, put the cock on a leading rein, and off we rode.

We got through the river with flying colours, for the bee was a good swimmer. When we came to the place where the maize had fallen into the water, we found that it had sprouted into such thick undergrowth that I did not know which way to go. I set spurs to the bee, and he jumped right over the maize forest. Unfortunately the cock jumped short and landed in the mud. There he quickly sank, until only his two eyes showed. The bee had to pull him out.

By this time it was already dark. The cock flew into a tree, the bee found a crevice in a rock, and I took shelter behind a young umbrella thorn for the night.

The next day when I went to fetch the bee, I saw that in the night he had filled the entire crevice with honeycomb. I was so pleased that I grabbed the black cock and rushed home for jugs and basins in which to keep the honey. But the cock was worn out, and halfway home I had to unsaddle him. He quickly laid an egg in the sand and hatched out a white cockerel. Him I harnassed to a Scotch-cart and drove it back to the honey nest.

It took toil and trouble to load the honey. As soon as I broke away one of the combs the bee had made two new ones. I had to stop him, or I would have loaded the cart to breaking point.

In the end I put the piebald bee under my tall hat and fastened the black cock to the back of the Scotch-cart. Then the little white cock in front had to strain at the tether.

I only got home three days later, and by then I was eleven months older than my father. I had scarcely swallowed my first cup of coffee when a messenger on a young rabbit stopped at the door. He said the farmers by the river sent word that I must come to harvest my maize, otherwise they were going to impound it.

"Impound away," said my father. "We're bee farmers. What have we to do with maize?"

"I don't know, Father," I said. "Maize grows well in that part of the world."

"Well, go then, if you must," said he.

So it happened that I became the biggest maize farmer in the Free State. There was never any trouble with draught cattle. At ploughing time I went and chose a few teams of bees at my father's. And there was never a farmer with such hardworking helpers as my black cock, my little cockerel and my piebald bee.

Sikulume
A Sotho tale

Long, long ago there was a chief who had eight sons. Seven of them were the bravest of the brave. Indeed, to tell the sad truth, they were too brave, and all seven fell on the battlefield. But the eighth, the youngest, was born mute, and he never learnt to talk. Sikulume was dumb.

The chief was very proud of his seven sons, and long did he mourn them. Then it happened that one day an old man of the tribe brought him the news that he had seen seven beautiful birds with long tails and crested heads at the cattle kraal.

"It's good that you told me, old one," said the chief. "Your reward

165

shall be seven fat cows. I've
lost seven sons, and these
birds shall be like children to
me. I shall send seven young
men out immediately to catch
them."

He called the young men of
the kraal together and chose
six of them. The seventh one who
was to catch a bird of his own,
was his youngest son – Sikulume.
He told him, "Do not appear before
me again until you bring me one of
these birds." This he said also to
each of the other young men.

For three long days the
young men journeyed through the
land, but the birds kept in front of them in the air
or in the trees. But the third night the birds roosted
in a small bush, because there were no high trees near. The
young men crept up on them and caught them, one by one.

"You beautiful bird," said the first young man to the bird he
had caught, and he stroked its crested head.

"You beautiful bird," said the second young man to the bird
he had caught, and he stroked its long tail.

"You beautiful bird," said all the others.

Sikulume was troubled. He held the bird that he had caught
close to him and he said with all his heart, "You beautiful
bird." Then his lips formed the words and his tongue suddenly awoke. "You beautiful bird," he said aloud. So it was that
Sikulume learnt to talk.

The next morning they began the return journey. They
chose the short cut over the plains, for now there were no birds
in front, leading them from tree to tree. That evening they
came to a hut.

"Let us sleep here," said Sikulume, and they went to sleep. In the depth of the night Sikulume woke with a start and he saw the shining eye of the full moon peering in at the door. "How is that possible?" he asked himself. "I shut the door myself yesterday evening." Just as he was about to get up and look, he heard a voice. It was a deep voice; it was an ugly voice. And the voice said, "Ha! I smell tender young meat. We can begin on this side with the one with the small feet. Then we can eat till we come to the other side. I'll just go and call my friends."

The owner of the voice stole away quietly, but because he was so big, his footsteps thundered dum, dum, dum! on the ground. Sikulume woke his friends and told them. "A cannibal

was here, and he's coming back. We must flee!" While he was speaking, he examined their feet and saw that his were the smallest.

Woa! His friends were more than a little scared. They jumped up and ran and ran through the night. But when they finally stopped to get their breaths back Sikulume saw that his hands were empty, and he realised that he had left his bird in the hut. "I must go back," he said, "for I may not appear before my father without the bird."

"Take mine," said one of the other young men, for they all loved Sikulume.

"Or mine," said another.

"Or mine. Or mine," the rest said.

"No," said Sikulume, "for the one who gives me his will also not be able to appear before the chief." He took his stick and stuck it in the ground in front of them. "So long as this remains upright," he said, "you'll know that I'm still alive. If it moves, you'll know I'm running. But if it falls over, you'll know that I'm dead."

Then he went back to the land of the cannibals. He came to the hut without being seen. He caught the bird without being heard. But, just as he was going out of the door, there was something crackle-crackling in the bushes. Even before he looked, he knew that the cannibals had come back. Whew! They were horrible! One shining eye on their foreheads, a mouth full of yellow fangs, one leg to stand on. But with that one leg, they could surely run. Sikulume ran lightly and quickly on his small feet, but the cannibals came ever nearer. He felt their warm breaths on the back of his neck. He heard them galloping thunderously at his heels – boom, boom, boom!

He pulled his skin kaross off and threw it on the ground. The kaross took one direction, and he took another. The cannibals chose wrongly. There they went, away after the kaross, boom, boom, boom! over the ground. The kaross could not keep ahead. They caught it and ate it up.

Meanwhile Sikulume was gaining ground. While the cannibals were still devouring the last bits of skin, Sikulume was
back with his friends. They stood in a ring around his kerrie,
which was shaking like a reed. "Hau! Sikulume," they greeted
him, "with your dove feet, you run as fast as thought."

"Eagles have to use their feet. There come the cannibals,"
warned Sikulume.

But it was the last time the cannibals saw them. All that
remained of the young men was a dust cloud on the plain. By
the time it settled, they were safe in the kraal. The cannibals
had to find other food.

The chief's heart was glad when they brought him the seven
birds. "I'll give you your own kraal, Sikulume," said he. "You'll
become a great chief."

"Then I'll take my six friends as my councillors," decided
Sikulume.

And that is what happened.

The clever little man
A Xhosa tale

I. The chief's son

It is said that long, long ago there was a chief who had no children. He and his people were sad at heart about this. So they said to each other, "Let's slaughter an ox and see if that helps." While they were still busy at the cattle kraal, a son was born to the chief. But he was not like other children. He was no bigger that a man's thumb, yet his face was old and wrinkled.

"Shu, Mother," said Tiny, "I'm cold. Please give me a kaross."

"Hau! You can talk already!" exclaimed his mother. "I've never heard that a newly born child could use his tongue like this." But she gave him a kaross.

Tiny went to the cattle kraal where the men were slaughtering the ox and said, "Father, I'm hungry. Give me some meat."

"Hau!" exclaimed the chief. "I've never heard of a newly born child eating meat." He gave him a piece of liver. But Tiny did not want liver. The chief gave him a bit of fat, but Tiny threw it away. He asked for meat. "Give him some," said the men. So the chief did, and Tiny was content.

After they had finished slaughtering the ox, the men asked each other, "Who'll take the meat to our homes?"

Tiny said, "I'm the man who'll carry the meat."

The men only laughed. "How can a small thing like you carry an ox?" they said.

Tiny said, "I'm stronger than all of you."

The men would not listen. They tried to pick up the carcass, but no one could move it.

"I'm the man who carries the meat," Tiny said again, and he

lifted the whole carcass on his shoulders. Then he walked off with it to the kraal.

Tiny was not only strong, oh no! He had his wits about him too. He went from one hut to another and left a trail of blood, but the meat he put in a huge pot on his mother's fire.

When the men came home, there was no meat. They called Tiny.

"I put the meat down there," said Tiny, and he pointed to the blood.

"Yes, we can see the trail," they said.

"The dogs must've eaten it," said Tiny.

"It must've been the dogs' doing," the men agreed, and they were very angry. They never thought that Tiny might have tricked them.

That night, when everyone slept, Tiny got up quietly and went to his mother's meat pot. He gobbled so greedily that his mother woke up. She grabbed a stick because she thought a dog was at the meat. Tiny ran out of the door on all fours, yelping like a dog, and his mother was content. Later that night Tiny came back, very quietly, and ate all the meat. The next morning the chief was furious because there was no meat to be found anywhere.

2. Tiny's plan

The chief called his men together. "We'll have to kill another ox," said he, "since the other one has disappeared."

"A good idea," they agreed.

They picked out a fat ox, slaughtered it and put the meat in a big pot. But Tiny was hungry again. He sat on a stone to think how he could get his hands on this meat also.

All at once he got up. He drove the cattle quietly into thick wood, where he tied their tails so that they could not move. With branches of thorns, he tore deep scratches in his arms and legs. Then he ran up to the men where they sat around a bit pot, keeping an eye on the meat to see that it did not grow legs again.

He screamed at them, "What do you think you're doing, sitting around the meat pot? The enemy came with a big army and drove off all our cattle!"

"Are you sure?" they asked.

"Just look at my arms and legs. I fought them, but there were too many," Tiny declared.

Then they saw the blood and believed him. They sprang up, grabbed their weapons and took off for the mountains in the direction he had indicated. It was, of course, completely wrong. On that track they would find no cattle.

By the fire there remained only one old man who could no longer fight. To him Tiny said, "Old man, I'm very tired and thirsty. Please, get me a little water from the river."

The old man was sorry for him and went off with a clay pot to the place where they drew water. And while he was away, Tiny pulled the pot off the fire and ate up all the meat.

3. How Tiny became a cattle farmer

When the chief found out at last how his son had cheated him, he was very angry and declared, "You'll get no more meat in this kraal."

Tiny answered, "Then I must start my own herd, for I can't do without meat."

He caught some birds in a trap, roasted them over a fire and ate the lot, except for the heads. When no one was looking, he hid these in the herdboys' knapsacks. He followed the boys when they set out and in the veld he confronted them and said, "You ate the birds that the chief's son caught."

"No, we did not," said the herdboys.

"What are those then, there in your knapsacks?" he asked.

They looked and they were frightened, for there lay the birds' heads.

"Now you must give me a digging stick," said Tiny, and they could not refuse.

Tiny went off with the stick to the river where the women were busy digging out clay to make pots.

"Why don't you borrow my digging stick?" asked Tiny.

But they had hardly stuck the stick in the clay when it snapped.

"Now you've broken my digging stick," said Tiny, "the digging stick that I got from the herdboys, the herdboys who ate the birds, the birds that the chief's son caught."

The women gave him a clay pot for the stick. With it he went to the goatherds who were busy drinking from the goats for their midday meal. Tiny said, "Why don't you borrow my clay pot? Then you could milk the goats and drink better."

"Lend it to us then," said the goatherds.

But when they lifted the pot, it cracked right across.

"Now you've cracked my clay pot," said Tiny, "the clay pot that the women gave me, the women who broke the digging stick, the digging stick that I got from the herdboys, the herdboys who ate the birds, the birds that the chief's son caught."

The goatherds gave him a goat for the clay pot. With that he went to the boys who looked after the calves. Tiny said, "Why don't you have a drink from my goat? Then you need not sit here with empty bellies."

"Let's drink from your goat then," said the boys.

But when they wanted to catch the goat, it ran away.

"Now you've chased my goat away," said Tiny, "the goat that the goatherds handed to me, the goatherds who cracked the clay pot, the clay pot that the women gave me, the women who broke the digging stick, the digging stick that I got from the herdboys, the herdboys who ate the birds, the birds that the chief's son caught."

The boys gave him a calf for the goat. With it, he went to the kraal where the men were busy milking. Tiny said, "Why don't you let my calf drink? Then the cows will give their milk more quickly."

"Give us your calf to suck," the men said.

But just when the calf took the teat in its mouth, it fell to the ground, stone-dead.

"Now you've killed my calf," said Tiny, "the calf that the boys gave me, the boys who chased my goat away, the goat that the

goatherds handed to me, the goatherds who cracked the clay pot, the clay pot that the women gave me, the women who broke the digging stick, the digging stick that I got from the herdboys, the herdboys who ate the birds, the birds that the chief's son caught."

The men gave him a cow for the calf, and Tiny was satisfied. "Now I'm a cattle farmer," he said, "and I don't have to ask anyone's permission when I want a bite of meat."

The tug of war

Hare took Elephant by surprise in the veld one day. "Move along," he said, talking big and full of swagger. He began to feed right under elephant's nose.

"Get out of my way, you little show-off," Elephant said crossly.

"Don't talk to me like that," answered Hare. "I'm much stronger than you are."

"Stronger than me!" jeered Elephant. "You can't be serious."

"Well," said Hare, "if you won't believe me, we can easily try a little tug of war. Then you'll see."

"Bring the rope," growled Elephant. "I've had enough of your boasting."

"Here it is," said Hare, and he rummaged about behind the bush where he had hidden the rope quite a while ago. "Just hold the one end tight, but don't start pulling until I give a little tug."

"All right," said Elephant.

Hare was away like the wind and ran down to the river. There Hippopotamus lay on a sandbank, asleep. "Just look at that old hippo," mocked Hare. "He's so fat and lazy from doing nothing that even a hare's too strong for him."

Hippo opened his eyes. "What did you say?" he growled angrily.

"I said what I said – and you heard me very well. I dare you to have a tug of war with me. Then you'll see that I speak the truth," said Hare.

"Here, give me the rope. I'll show you," bellowed Hippo, and up he stood.

"Come along," said Hare. "My rope's just over that hill."

Hare shot off, with Hippo following at a clumsy trot. "Here it is," said Hare. "Hold fast and don't pull before I give a little tug."

"Get a move on," said Hippo. "I'm in a hurry. "I've got to put in a lot more sleep before I feed tonight."

Hare loped off to the crest of the hill. He looked down at Elephant and Hippo standing on either side and laughed happily to himself. Then he tugged at the rope, and Elephant and Hippo fell to it.

It was really something. Elephant started by walking off, for how could Hare hold him back? But Hippo dug in and the real pulling began. Elephant ploughed four great furrows in the ground. The skin on Hippo's stomach was scraped raw.

They could not go on for much longer. First Elephant stumbled, then Hippo slackened. One would have to give up.

"Oh no!" sighed Hippo at last, and he collapsed. The rope caught on his hind leg and Elephant pulled him over the hill.

"I told you, Hare!" trumpeted Elephant, rejoicing, "I told you I'm stronger than you."

But when he looked round, there was no Hare, only Hippo.

"What's been going on?" Elephant roared in rage. "Are you trying to play games with me?"

"No, no," pleaded Hippo, for he was still too tired to stand up. "I thought that I was having a tug of war with Hare."

"I don't believe you," declared Elephant. "You and that nuisance Hare thought of this trick to make fun of me, but luckily I was too strong for you." He charged at poor Hippo and bit his tail off short. "Let that be a lesson to you not to pick a fight with someone like me," he shouted as he went off, trunk held high.

Dejected and miserable, Hippo struggled back to the river. He had always been so proud of his beautiful, curly tail. When he got back to the water and saw all the young hippos cutting a dash with their tails in the air, he got so cross that he rushed at them. One by one he bit off their tails, as Elephant had done to him. From that day to this hippos have no tails at all.

Every which way

Early one morning Jackal came to drink at Crab's house.

"Morning, Jackal," said Crab. "Nice morning, eh?"

"Very nice," replied Jackal, who had eaten his fill the night before. "I could run a mile."

"Well, let's run then," said Crab.

"You? You couldn't keep pace with me for half a step," said Jackal rudely.

"We'll see," said Crab.

"Come then," said Jackal, and he raced off beside the water-course. He did not realise that Crab had quietly gripped his tail fast in his big claws.

When Jackal thought that he had run far enough, he called over his shoulder, "Now, Crab, where are you?"

"Here," Crab answered, right behind him.

"How did you get there?" Jackal asked in surprise.

"I ran," replied Crab.

"Run a bit, so that I can see," said Jackal.

Crab trotted off, sideways and backwards and sideways again, just as crabs always do.

"Well," said Jackal, "it's no wonder that you kept up with me. You can run every which way, while we other animals can only move in one direction."

Jackal and Wolf
1. The barrel of butter

Jackal and Wolf were walking along, walking along, walking along the road when they came across a cartload of barrels stacked high. "Aha," said Jackal, "I know about those barrels. They're full of butter."

Wolf's mouth began to water. "Can't we pinch one, Jackal?" he asked.

"Why not?" said Jackal. "You go ahead, lie in the road and play dead. Farmer will pick you up and put you on the cart. Then you roll a barrel off quietly. I'll hide in the grass and do the rest."

"Fine," said Wolf, and away he ran. He had not been lying long in the road, when Farmer stopped beside him. "Ho, ho!" said Farmer, "now I wonder, is this wolf as dead as he looks?" and he gave Wolf a few good cuts with his whip to make sure.

Wolf did not bat an eyelid. "All right," said Farmer. "It looks as if he's done for. I'll take him home and skin him." And he threw Wolf up behind on the kegs and drove off.

Wolf lay dead still. What if Farmer looked round? Slowly he sat up. Whew, he was sore! He ached all over. Then he smelt the butter and forgot his pains. Quickly he pushed a barrel off and jumped down after it. Jackal ran up, boasting. "That was a good idea of mine, eh, Wolf?" he said as they rolled the keg into the bushes. "He'll never know what happened to his butter."

"Come on," said Wolf. "Let's get at it. I can't wait any longer."

This really shocked Jackal. "Wolf," he said, "you can't eat such fresh butter. It will kill you. It's got to ripen first."

So they hid the barrel and ran off home.

On the second day, as Wolf was lying in the sun by his door,

dreaming of the butter, he saw Jackal going past. "Jackal," called Wolf, "how about that butter? It must be ready now."

"I can't be bothered with butter," said Jackal. "Can't you see I'm in a hurry? My wife's had a child, and today I must get him christened."

"What are you going to call him?" Wolf asked inquisitively.

"Just Begun," said Jackal, and he staggered off. He had been hard at it that morning, and his stomach was so full of butter, he could hardly walk.

Wolf waited a few days, then he could stand it no longer. He stopped Jackal again. "What about the butter, Jackal?" he asked.

Jackal was really upset. "You won't believe it, Wolf," he said, "but I have another child to christen."

"What's his name to be?" Wolf was curious. He'd found the odd name of Jackal's first child very amusing.

"First Hoop," said Jackal. He had that very morning eaten the butter down to the first band on the barrel.

And so it went on, week after week. Whenever Wolf asked, Jackal had another child to christen: Second Hoop, Third Hoop, Fourth Hoop – the whole string. Wolf was at his wits' end. He thought of nothing but butter. He dreamt of nothing else.

"Come now," said Jackal one morning, "tomorrow, my friend, we'll definitely go. I had my last child christened today."

"I suppose this time it's called Seventh Hoop," said Wolf. He was so fed up that the names of Jackal's children no longer seemed funny.

"Oh no," Jackal said with a groan. Its name is All Gone."

Early next morning Jackal was there as he had promised, and the two set out for the butter keg.

"My friend, that butter's going to taste good," said Jackal.

"Yes," said Wolf, and he went a bit faster.

"It will be as ripe as butter could be," said Jackal.

"Yes, yes," said wolf, and he began to run.

"I can already feel it melting away," Jackal went on.

This time Wolf did not answer. His mouth was watering so much that he could not get a word out.

They came to the barrel and opened it. The butter was all gone.

"Oh no!" groaned Jackal.

"Oh no!" groaned Wolf.

"You ate it!" said Jackal.

"No, you did!" said Wolf.

Oh, bother and oh, brother! One word led to another.

"I'll beat you black and blue!"

"I'll murder you!"

Wolf raised his fist to lay Jackal out. Jackal hurriedly got out of range. "Wait, wait, my friend!" he begged. Wolf was bigger and stronger than he, and if it came to a fight he would certainly be the loser. "All this talk of beating and murder is unnecessary. Let's rather try to find out quietly who the guilty one is."

"It's you!" shouted Wolf.

"Well, I think you're the one," said Jackal smugly. "Let's go and lie in the sun and see whose mouth drips butter. Then we'll know for sure."

"And that one will get a good hiding," growled Wolf, certain of his innocence.

"You bet!" agreed Jackal.

They lay down in the sun. It was not long before Wolf was snoring, fit to wake the dead. Quietly Jackal got up, scraped the last of the butter out with a stick and rubbed it round Wolf's mouth. Then he lay down again.

It was a real treat to see what happened when they woke.

"My mouth is clean," Jackal announced with satisfaction.

"I'm the buttery one," gasped Wolf.

191

"Then we know where the trouble lies," said Jackal as he went to pick a tough cane.

"I must've eaten the butter in my sleep," Wolf said as he stood meekly to receive his punishment, "because I don't remember a thing about it."

And Jackal dusted his jacket thoroughly.

2. Jackal and Wolf in the sheep kraal

Wolf was hungry. For days now the hunting had gone badly. When he was stalking a herd of springbuck, already imagining the taste of the warm meat between his teeth, what happened? He trod upon a bustard that flew cackling out of the grass, and all was in vain. Or when he was about to take a blesbuck by surprise and all was going according to plan, the breeze suddenly changed its direction. The buck got wind of him and made tracks. No, the world was full of misery, and life was not worth living. Just then Jackal came running by.

"What's happening, Jackal?" asked Wolf.

"I'm going to kill myself a fatted lamb," said Jackal. "Won't you come along?"

Wolf shook his head sadly. "Where do you get fatted lambs nowadays?" he asked. "Farmer's got too clever for us. Since he's built that stone kraal, we can't get at them any more."

"The wall's too high, and the gate's too tight. This I know," said Jackal. "But have you forgotten the draining holes?"

"You think we can get in there?" asked Wolf, becoming a bit more hopeful.

"I know we can," replied Jackal. "I was there yesterday evening."

"Then why didn't you mention it sooner?" asked Wolf, and he set off at once.

It was a long way and the moon was already up before they came to the kraal, but Wolf made nothing of the distance.

"Careful now," whispered Jackal. "As soon as we're in, we must each pull down our lamb with the first blow so that the flock doesn't take fright and kick up a racket. Then Farmer's dogs will hear us."

"That's right," said Wolf.

They slipped in through the draining holes. Yes, Wolf was so thin that he got in quite easily. It was just, "Hello, how're you?" before two lambs lay with their legs in the air and Wolf and Jackal were tasting tender young meat. Wolf was so hungry that he thought only of stuffing himself, but Jackal was wary. Every so often he went to the draining hole to make sure that he could still get through. When he saw that this was it – another mouthful, and he would stick fast – he made tracks and left Wolf alone in the kraal.

Wolf ate up his own lamb. When he saw Jackal had gone, he put his leftovers away too. He was full to bursting. Groaning, he staggered to the draining hole and tried to creep out. But he was in great trouble. He tried this way, and he tried that way. He turned himself on the one side, and he turned himself on the other side. His stomach was just too big.

This was what Jackal was waiting for. When he saw that there was no way Wolf could get out, he ran off and called, "Farmer, Farmer, come quickly! Wolf is in you sheep kraal."

"Hey, Jackal, what are you up to?" shouted Wolf anxiously. He dived with all his might into the draining hole, and there he got stuck.

"Farmer, Farmer!" shouted Jackal.

The dogs began to bark.

"Come quickly!" yelled Jackal.

The back door opened.

"In the sheep kraal!" laughed Jackal, and he made off.

Poor Wolf, this was not what a friend should do to you. When Farmer came to the kraal and saw what was going on, he went to fetch his sjambok.

"So ho!" Whack! "You, eh?" Whack! "I'll teach you . . ." Whack! Wallop! Whack! Farmer gave Wolf a good dressing-down, while Wolf could only beg for mercy, though he knew it was useless.

When he was tired of thrashing, Farmer dragged Wolf out of the draining hole, flung him out at the gate and called, "Get him!" to his dogs so that they could finish what he begun. But that drubbing was enough for Wolf. He was not going to let himself be torn to pieces. Like a bullet out of a gun he shot over the rise, and the dogs never saw him again.

That was the last time that Wolf tried to steal Farmer's sheep.

3. The hanging rock

Now Wolf had had enough of Jackal and his schemes. He swore murder if he should get hold of him. Jackal had to stay on the move. The game kept on for weeks, for Wolf could not hunt Jackal day and night. He had to find food in-between. So Jackal breathed more freely because he kept out of Wolf's clutches quite easily.

One sunny day Jackal was lying high in a narrow ravine under the shade of a big rock hanging overhead. There had been hare's meat for lunch, and a mouthful of honey for desert. Life was good, and it was good to be alive. He yawned thrice, then he was dead to the world.

The sun was already touching the hills when he woke with a start. He did not stretch as he usually stretched. He did not yawn his three yawns. No, he smelt trouble. He peered down into the ravine and saw his predicament. Wolf was loping up towards him. Jackal looked around quickly. Only bushes and cliffs everywhere. This time he could not escape. He would have to use his wits. Like lightning he shot up and stood with his forefeet against the overhanging rock. He groaned softly like someone who was bearing too heavy a load and could hold out no longer.

"Aha!" yelled Wolf when he spotted him. "Yesterday's gone, and tomorrow will come, but today you're as dead as mutton." He was all set to rip Jackal to pieces, but Jackal gasped, "Be careful, friend Wolf. This rock is about to collapse. If I let go now we're both flat pancakes."

"Heavens!" said Wolf, and he moved back quickly. "Why didn't you say so?"

"But I did . . . Help!" Jackal's legs seemed to give a little. "Help, I can't hold it any longer."

Without thinking, Wolf dived forward and caught hold of the rock firmly.

"That's good," Jackal sighed with relief. "Now I can rest a bit."

"Don't leave me alone," begged Wolf. "I can feel that it's a very heavy rock."

"I'll go quickly to get an axe so that we can chop a few poles to support the rock," Jackal answered, and he loped off.

"Don't waste any time!" Wolf called after him.

"I won't," replied Jackal. "I always make use of my opportunities." And he moved even faster.

Wolf stood the whole of that night and through the next morning, but Jackal did not return.

Baboon was the first to come by. "What's up now, Wolf?" he asked.

"This rock's about to collapse, and I must hold it up," replied Wolf. "Jackal's gone to fetch an axe so that we can cut some props. But I wonder where he could be staying such a long time."

"His axe must be blunt," said Baboon, and he went off.

Duiker trotted up the ravine. "What's going on?" he asked curiously. So Wolf had to tell the whole story again.

"He must've lost the handle," said Duiker, and he went off.

Then, just about midday, Vulture came by and sat down on the rock.

"Don't do that!" yelled Wolf. "The thing's heavy enough already."

"Heavy enough?" asked Vulture, and he moved off to the branch of a nearby tree.

"Yes, very heavy," replied Wolf. "I can hardly keep it up." He explained everything to Vulture. "But Jackal's axe must surely be lost, otherwise he would've been back long ago," he added.

Then Vulture began to laugh. "The rock's falling – ka, ka, ka! Jackal's axe – ke, ke, ke! The axe is lost – ko, ko, ko!"

"What's the matter with you, Vulture? How can you sit there laughing at me?" Wolf asked crossly. "What are you trying to say?"

"I'm trying to say – he, he, he! The rock won't fall – ho, ho, ho! Jackal never went to fetch an axe – ha, ha, ha! Jackal himself is lost and gone – ho, ho, ho!" answered Vulture.

"I've got a good mind to grab you off that branch and pull your tail feathers out, one by one," yelled Wolf furiously, and he sprang at the branch where Vulture sat.

"He, he, he!" laughed Vulture as he flew lazily upwards. "There, you've let go of the rock, and it hasn't fallen."

Wolf looked at the rock, and he looked at his forefeet. He saw that Vulture spoke the truth.

Then he realised that Jackal had fooled him again.

Antjie Somers

Andries Somers was the best fisherman in the Strand. Who could hold a trawl net as firmly as he? Who could row a boat as he could? No one! – And brave! When anyone was in danger, Andries Somers was the first to help. He could swim like a fish. When everyone else had given in to despair, he alone saved countless souls from drowning.

But envy is rife, and it is easy to pick a quarrel. One day a number of fishermen attacked him on the beach. Andries was not one to be trifled with. They were bowled over by his fists. And one of them lay very still where his head had hit against a rock. Andries had to flee, or else run the risk of hanging. He got a dress from his sister. He tied a scarf round his head. He put a basket on his arm. Then he headed far into the interior of the country.

He found a new home on a farm beyond the mountains. As before, he worked with a will. From morning to night he slogged away. Digging in the vineyard or harvesting grapes or manuring the ground, it was all the same to him. Andries Somers became the foreman on the farm.

But envy has long ears, and a story has many tongues. Before long people were hard at gossiping among themselves.

"Tell us about the dress that you've hidden in your house," one hinted slyly. "And the head scarf, Andries Somers? Or perhaps your name is Antjie?" teased another.

"Antjie Somers! Antjie Somers!" they mocked him.

Andries Somers hung his head and pretended not to hear, for if he answered, there would only be another brawl. But after the teasing had gone on for three days, he could bear it no more. That evening he packed his bundle and left.

He never came back. His tracks were never found. He had vanished into thin air.

But, more and more frequently, the children who went out to get wood on the mountain told of an old woman who chased them.

"She has a red scarf on her head," said one child.

"She wears a dress with big stripes."

"She has a long knife."

"And a basket."

"And a grain-sack on her shoulder."

"She'll catch us and put us in her sack," they wailed.

The grown-ups shook their heads. "It's that Antjie Somers," they said to one another.

Andries Somers was forgotten: the brave one, the hard-working one, he who was always the best. Only one story was repeated ever louder, from generation to generation. "Antjie Somers! Antjie Somers! Antjie Somers will get you!"

The witch of the valley

Elise was a pretty girl. There was no one like her in the whole Hex River valley. But, sad to say, she was as proud as she was beautiful. When the young men came courting her, she tossed her head and said, "Only the best, the most handsome and hard-working young man is fit to be my husband."

One day Philip rode up to the farm on his chestnut horse. His laughter was pleasant on the ear. He was good to look at, and he was not afraid of work. Elise knew then that this was the young man she had waited for. Still she was haughty and hard to please. "Go and pick me the blood-red disa that grows on the highest crag," said she. "Then I'll know that you're worthy of my love."

Philip said that he would go.

He climbed and climbed and, as he climbed, he sang.

He climbed and climbed with a laugh in his heart and on his lips.

He climbed until he was among the highest crags. There, far above, on the top of a rock that hung over the deepest precipice, the red disa bloomed.

"Now I'm going to pick you," said Philip, "for my bride is waiting for me."

But when he bent forward the rock crumbled under his feet. He reached out, but all he could grasp was the flower, and with the disa in his hand, he plunged to his death below.

When Elise heard of his death, her heart broke. "Philip, Philip!" she wept, but it was too late. "Philip, Philip!" she cried, but to no avail. "Philip, Philip!" she called, and she set out to climb the mountain to the place where the blood-red disa had grown.

When she saw the broken stalk and the signs of Philip's fall, she was overcome with despair. "Philip, Philip!" she sighed and sank to the ground. And the precipice claimed her, as it had claimed Philip, and she fell to her death.

Even now, people say, you can see her wandering there, although only a spectre remains of her. Her sigh is but a breath of wind. But she cannot find peace. Every moonlit night she comes to seek her Philip again, even though she will never find him.

"That's her just reward," people say. "Her pride cost a young man his life. She's a witch."

And that was how the most beautiful girl of the Hex River valley became the witch of the valley.

How Wolf learnt to fly

Wolf was faint with hunger. Every time he got to a carcass, Vulture had long disposed of the best bits and only the bare bones remained.

"Vulture, how is it that you know so quickly where there's something to eat?" whined Wolf.

"That's simple," replied Vulture. "I fly high in the air and can look far over the countryside. You can only see the bushes in front of your nose."

"Teach me to fly," begged Wolf.

"All right," said Vulture. "Climb on my back, then you can see exactly what I do."

Vulture spread his powerful wings, and Wolf clung tight.

"Do you see, Wolf?" called out Vulture as they glided high over a patch of thorn bush. "It's easy. Now you jump off and flap with your legs as I flap my wings."

Wolf dived through the air, but although he kicked and kicked with all his strength, he fell like a stone, right into the thorn bushes.

"Ou-ou-ouch!" he howled as he struggled out from among the clutching branches.

"Let that be a lesson to you," called Vulture from on high. "An animal's made to run, and a bird's made to fly. Animals who try to do otherwise, only get into difficulties."

Rainier de Winnaar
I. Strong tobacco

Because I was such an exceptional man (said Rainier), Satan tried hard to herd me into his own kraal. First, there was this plan, then there was that trick, until I became annoyed with the business. One day I sat, as usual, leaning against the river bank with my pipe between my teeth and Shooting Star, my gun, on my knee. I was waiting to see if perhaps one or two

ducks did not want to seek their death. Suddenly Satan stood before me.

"Morning, Rainier," he said. "You're very comfortable there."

"Morning, Satan," I replied. "I would be even more comfortable if you didn't stand in my sun."

"Excuse me," said Satan, and he moved back a little. "I only want to know if you can perhaps provide me with a fill of tobacco."

"Sure," I said, for my plans were made. "And a pipe and a lighter as well."

"That's very good of you," said Satan. "I'm beginning to like you more and more."

Of course, it is not such a good sign when Satan starts liking you, and I decided to finish the business off quickly. "Just open your mouth so that I can put the pipe in," I said.

Satan opened up. I lifted Shooting Star and pushed him into Satan's cheek and pulled the trigger. There was just one crack, then the fumes and smoke shot out of Satan's ears.

"Oho!" said Satan, and he shook his head. "Your lighter makes a terrible noise."

"That's the only kind of lighter I have," I said.

"What on earth . . .?"

said Satan, and he spat the bits of lead from my slugs out behind the bushes. "It seems to me that your pipe's stem is broken."

"You've bitten the tip off," I said.

"Heavens!" said Satan, and he sniffed the air. "Your tobacco's very strong."

"I always smoke strong tobacco," I said.

With that Satan fell down, head over heels, so that only his horns stuck out above the clumps of grass. But when I got up, ready to skin him, he was gone, and all there was left was a burnt patch where he had fallen. Unfortunately the scoundrel did not die from that strong tobacco, because I see his work everywhere around me in this old world. But since that day he has never bothered me again.

2. Catchem

War came to the land and, because the people knew what was good for them, they immediately made me a field general. At once I leapt on my horse with my sabre at my side, for a field general has only to make sure that everything goes well. There are enough ordinary burghers to do the shooting.

In this fashion I rode through the veld, with Catchem, my faithful dog, by my side, until a buck sprang away through the bushes, and Catchem went after it. The buck, however, kept ahead, and at length I became anxious to rejoin my burghers before there was any trouble.

"Move over, Catchem!" I yelled and drew my sabre and gave my horse the reins. Only three strides and I was next to the buck. I struck. The dratted dog did not dodge quickly enough, and I cut him right through the middle, from his snout to the tip of his tail.

Immediately I jumped off my horse and pressed the two halves of my dog neatly together again. Unfortunately I was in a bit of a hurry, and so I accidentally joined him upside down. So there Catchem stood, with two paws on the ground and two paws in the air.

"Wait a minute, Catchem," I said, but the dog did not have time. He shot away like a bullet from a gun and overtook the buck – one, two, three. When the one pair of paws got tired, he just turned himself over and ran on the other pair. You could say that from that day onwards I had two dogs in one.

The Flying Dutchman

For days the storm raged over land and sea. People scarcely dared to go out of doors. The ships lay anchored in the harbour.

A captain paced the deck of his merchant ship, up and down, up and down. The wind tore at him; high waves washed around his feet. He clenched his fist and shouted, "Away! Away! I must set out to see!" But the wind quenched his words.

Hendrik Vanderdecken was the most famous captain who plied the Dutch trade with the Far East. No one could sail a ship around the Cape of Good Hope faster than he. No one returned home with a load of spices before him. He knew only one happiness, and that was on the wide waters. He had only one desire, and that was to sail.

Captain Vanderdecken called together his steersman and sailors. "Hoist the sails!" he said. "Haul up the anchor!"

"But the storm, Captain?" objected one.

"And it is Easter," urged another.

"Let the church keep its own festivals! Let the storm blow itself out! We're sailing!" shouted Hendrik Vanderdecken.

Laughing, his sailors clambered into the rigging. Joyfully they fastened the sails. Their captain spoke like a man. He was afraid of nothing. Long live Captain Vanderdecken!

But just as the ship was ready, the church bells began to ring. In great waves of sound the message went out, "Christ has risen. Christ has truly risen!"

"We're sailing!" yelled Captain Vanderdecken.

Then it happened. Suddenly the ship glowed blood red, as if a shaft of sunlight had broken through, yet overhead the dark clouds still whirled and twisted. The ship began to move, but in such a fashion as no man on earth had seen before: the sails filled full against the wind. And as she shot ever more swiftly over the water and out of the bay, a black bird dived through the mist and circled above her mast.

"Look!" called out the other captains in the harbour.

"Look!" shouted the workmen on the quay.

Dumbfounded they stared after Captain Vanderdecken and his ship.

The ship never arrived in the Far East. Never was she seen in her home port again. But travellers on the far seas brought strange reports back with them – stories of a ghost ship that sailed the water round the Cape of Good Hope. Her sails were filled against the wind, and a black bird circled around her mast, while blue fire shone out of the hollow eye sockets of the sailors lying on deck. Only the captain stood upright, his clenched fist held aloft; he seemed to be shouting, but no sound came from his lips. It had to be Vanderdecken.

Sailors feared that ship as they feared no other danger on the ocean, for woe betide the men who encountered it. Disaster would befall them before the moon was new: shipwreck, mutiny, or a storm that drove them onto the rocks. So the survivors reported, and they were never many.

Time went by. The tales grew. Once every seven years, the sailors whispered, life returned to the dead ship. You heard the anchor chain rattle as she came to lie alongside you. A hollow voice called, asking if you would take letters for home. Then a boat splashed into the water, the oarsmen pulled across, and a hand white as death delivered the packet.

They were strange letters, those. You should look at the addresses. They were for people long dead and gone. You should not delay, but nail the letters to the mast. Otherwise all the woes of the seas would beset you between one full moon and the next.

She still sails today, the seamen say. Sometimes, on a misty night, the ghost ship rises out of the waves and then, as always, you see the red glow, the black bird and the blue fire. It is Vanderdecken. He is sailing through the centuries on his *Flying Dutchman* because he once mocked God and his faith, and now he can find no rest for his soul.

Epilogue to the first edition

There exists in South Africa, as can only be expected from a country with such a rich diversity of peoples, a virtually unbelievable wealth of folk tales. Only think of the number of possibilities: true life stories, sagas, myths, legends, nursery tales ("fairy tales"), which include fables and jokes – the quick-fire stories, par excellence, for our hurried times. Today even nursery tales are made and remade in the form of jokes. As far as this collection is concerned, I need only mention the stories of "The stupid farmer" and "Strong tobacco", whose themes are often encountered purely as jokes. Indeed, the folk tale covers man's entire field of experience, with the world of the imagination added on as well.

We find in South Africa, therefore, stories that the forefathers of the white settlers brought with them out of Western Europe. There are stories from the East, chiefly brought here by the slaves, whose principal descendants are known today as the Cape Malays, and the Indians, who settled here in the nineteenth century. Then there are stories from Africa itself, from the old San and Khoikhoi races, from black slaves, chiefly from Madagascar and Mozambique, and from the various black peoples themselves. To the traditional stories from centuries-old sources must be added the new creations evolved over the years. As far as the main groups of Afrikaans and English speakers are concerned, these new contributions are numerous. Intensive research has revealed that, of nursery tales alone, about two-thirds have originated in this country. The percentage is even higher in the other categories.

As the title of the anthology indicates, this collection offers a small cross-section of the wealth of tales from most of the groups living in South Africa. What is more, there are so many categories of stories. At the outset we have to make a distinction between the report of an event and a story. For example, a mere rendering concerning an accident that befell you, cannot be regarded as a story. As in the literary short story, the folk tale demands that the facts be put together in such a fashion that there is an absorbing exposition and a climax. In other words, an element of imagination, an act of creation, comes into it. Then the truth test must be applied. True-life stories can concern any general incident that is presented as true: a hunting story, or the story of a comic or tragic love affair, or anything else. Sagas also count as true stories, but here the old folk beliefs about the supernatural must be included, as with ghost and ghoul stories. Myths are related to religion and can therefore be taken as true or untrue, depending upon your beliefs:

what the Christian accepts as true, does not hold for the Buddhist, and vice versa. Once legends were regarded as true-life stories. These were originally accepted by people as the truth, but later on lost their significance. Some tales were accepted from the beginning as "tall" stories with no claim to the truth. In nursery tales reality is disregarded, and the story creates its own imaginary world. Jokes can be based on real happenings, but are mostly fabrications.

In this edition "Antjie Somers" is a true-life story. Stories like "The witch of the valley" and "The Flying Dutchman" are sagas. "Sheikh Yussuf" is an example of a Cape Malay Islamic myth; on the other hand "Little Hare Harelip" is an old San myth. "The seal maiden" and "The Enchanted Forest" (Khoikhoi) are legends, as are the "tall" stories: "The disappearance of the piebald bee" and the tales of Rainier de Winnaar. "The ungrateful snake", "Pinkie", "The war between the animals and the birds" and many more, are nursery tales in their pure form. "Bluebottle and Bee" and "The incompetent judge" are fables, that is to say, nursery tales with an implicit moral.

Looking at it from another angle, this book also presents a cross-section of different groups that have contributed to the

treasury of South African stories. The greatest number of stories originated from the heirs to the West European tradition, both white and brown (the whole cycle woven round the struggle between the animals, birds and insects, as well as the Owlglass stories, the stories about Jackal and Wolf, and others). Then there are San stories ("The great thirst", "The watersnake", "Little Hare Harelip", etc.), a Khoikhoi story ("The Enchanted Forest"), and stories from the black peoples (Sikulume, "The clever little man", etc.).

Seen from yet another angle, this collection contains, on the one hand, stories which embody the influence of the West European mother countries most strongly (for example, "The war between the animals and the birds", "How the birds chose a king", "The barrel of butter", "The Flying Dutchman", and others) and on the other hand, there is a powerful group of stories which originated here in South Africa ("Bluebottle and Bee", "The mouse who was too clever", "King Lion's presents", "The golden bird", "The cleft in the mountain", and many others).

Two of the most interesting stories in the book, which were incorporated into the treasury of South African stories as new creations, are undoubtedly "The witch of the valley" and "Captain Van Hunks and the Devil". Research has revealed that each of these stories has another story attached to it.

Firstly, "The witch of the valley": This sad tale is usually presented as if a child or children of French Huguenots could have been part of it. This would mean that if such an accident actually took place in the mountains, it had to have happened shortly after 1700. But if one researches the histories of the traditional farms and families, one finds that the only possible time is about 1840.

Secondly, "Captain Van Hunks and the Devil", the story of how Table Mountain got its tablecloth: This is supposedly based on an old Malay story from the days of the Dutch East India Company, that is to say, also somewhere before 1800. I have researched all the available information and have established that no such legend has existed before 1900. Everything points to the fact that the story is undoubtedly the creation of the English journalist and author, Ian D. Colvin, who lived in South Africa for several years. The story appears under the title, "How Table Mountain got its cloud" in his book *Romance of Empire: South Africa*, which was published in 1909. It caught on immediately and in the course of time became an attractive part of the store of South African folk tales.

Something needs to be said about the working methods followed in the retelling of the stories in this book. They can be summarised in a single phrase: an attempt to recreate the stories as folk tales. For the nursery tales, a simple, yet rhythmical style, with rhymes, repetition and a predilection for events happening in patterns of three was followed: the hare went three times to steal water, the "stupid" farmer outwitted the conceited students three times, and so on. The recreations were necessary because the form in which the stories was recorded was often unsatisfactory, as in the case of "The stupid farmer" mentioned above, "The cleft in the mountain", and many more. Of some, like "The seal maiden", "Bluebottle and Bee" and "Sheikh Yussuf", only the core remained from which a story had to be built. There are also many instances where several variations of one and the same story exist, none completely satisfactory; the basic elements of these were put together and refashioned in for example, "The ungrateful snake", "The war between the animals and the birds" and "How the animals chose a king". There is no standard form for even our most famous stories, such as "The witch of the valley". "Captain Van Hunks and the Devil" (of which, as I have indicated, I have discovered the original story) also acquired new turns and twists over the years. There is not even agreement about the old captain's name, and he turns up as Van Hunk, Van Honk, Van Donck or Van Donk, and even as Van Plots. One could therefore say that, with this collection, an attempt has been made to recreate a number of our most attractive folk tales, and to place them at the reader's disposal.

Obviously restoration is always a problem, albeit that of a building or some cultural heritage. Literally, the word means restoring something to its original form, but we all know that is impossible. Even after careful research a building or chair can never again look exactly the way it did originally. The years have passed and time has left its mark. In a story, the original form (if that can be traced at all, as in the extremely rare case of "Captain Van Hunks and the Devil") is even less important. The themes are handed down, but in reality a story only exists momentarily in the form in which it is told and its quality varies according to the capacities of the narrator. I therefore believe I have the right to be a narrator of South African folk tales and I hope that my imagination succeeded in making these stories vibrantly alive.

Pieter W. Grobbelaar
May 1984

224